John Penn and Sons

nwich

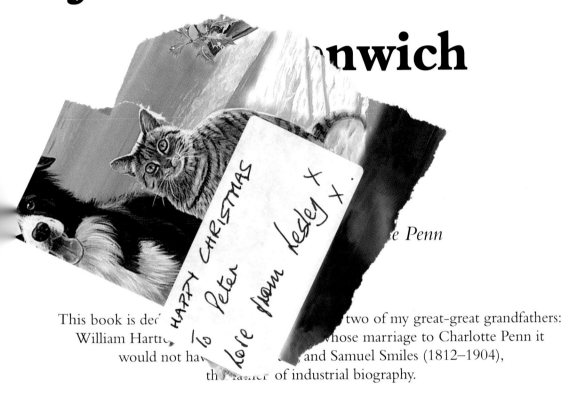

e Penn

This book is dec[...] two of my great-great grandfathers:
William Hartr[...] [w]hose marriage to Charlotte Penn it
would not ha[...] and Samuel Smiles (1812–1904),
th[e father] of industrial biography.

ISBN 13: 9-781-84306-411-4

Printed by: Gutenberg Press Ltd, Malta
Designed by: Sarah Labuhn
Edited by: Ian Howe

Front cover image: Portrait of John Penn II, on background the interior of Greenwich Works

Back cover image: Penn Almshouses, South Street, Greenwich

Designed by Landmark Publishing Ltd on behalf of Richard Hartree

John Penn and Sons of Greenwich

Richard Hartree

with an Epilogue by Prudence Penn

About the authors:

Richard Hartree, BA, CEng, FIMMM had a thirty-six-year, UK and international, technical and management career with the Alcan Aluminium Limited group. He is a member of the Council of the Association for Industrial Archaeology. His paternal great-great-grandfather married the daughter of the first John Penn and became a partner in the firm. Telling the firm's story created an opportunity for him to combine his interests in industrial and family history. He is a volunteer Small Business Advisor, an amateur French horn player and a less competent golfer.

Prudence Penn is the widow of Lt Col Sir Eric Penn, who was a great-great-grandson of the first John Penn, founder of the firm. He had a career first in the Grenadier Guards and then as Comptroller of the Lord Chamberlain's Office in the Queen's Household. Lady Penn became a lady-in-waiting to Queen Elizabeth The Queen Mother.

Acknowledgements

I thank the following individuals and institutions for their help, support and encouragement.

Individuals

Paul Blackburn, Pedro Campos, John Day, Peter Fitzgerald, Dick Garcia, Charles Gordon-Clarke, Brian Hillsdon, Johannes Hirsch, Michael Lommantzsch, Mike McCarthy, Robert Malster, Keith Moore, Prudence Penn, Dr Ursula Perkow, John Porter, Stuart Rankine, John Riley, Ray Riley, Neil Rhind, Bill Smith, Pieter Van der Merwe, Robert Vogel, Ron Woolacott, Michael Wright.

Institutions

Banbury Library, Bancroft Local History Library, Bodleian Library, British Library and National Newspaper Collection, Family Record Centre, Family History Centre, Family (Probate) Court, Greenwich Local History Library, Institution of Civil Engineers, Institution of Mechanical Engineers, Lewisham Local History Library, Metropolitan Records, National Archive, National Maritime Museum, National Science Museum Library and Collection, Royal Archive, Royal Society, HMS *Warrior* Preservation Trust, Western Australia Maritime Museum.

Illustrations

Thanks for permissions to reproduce copyright items are due to:
Chrysalis Books Group Plc, © Basil Greenhill and Ann Giffard, 1988. Reproduced from *The British Assault on Finland, a Forgotten Naval War*, Conway Maritime Press – 307.
© Chrysalis – 307
© Dover Museum – 402
© Greenwich Local History Library – 501
© Institution of Mechanical Engineers – 405
© Lewisham Local Studies Centre – 205, 407
© Malthouse Press – 201
© National Maritime Museum – 306, 403, 415, 416, 606, 701, IIa, IIb, IIIa
© Sächsische Dampfschiffahrt GmbH – 203
© Sambourne Collection – 413, 414
© Science and Society Picture Library – 309, 401, 406, 409

Thanks are also due for permission to use my own photographs of items in the ownership of:
Sächsische Dampfschiffahrt GmbH – IVa.
Southampton Maritime Museum – 601.
National Museum of Science and Industry (The Science Museum) – 305.
Warrior Preservation Trust – IIIb
Western Australia Maritime Museum – 307, IVb.

All other illustrations come from the authors' and other private collections. Special thanks to Bob Baldwin who drew the diagrams, Area Map and Works Layout.

Contents

Author's Preface 6

Penn Family Tree 1 7

Area Map 8

Chapter 1.   Background and Early Years (1770–1825) 9

Chapter 2.   Into Steam (1825–1843) 19

Chapter 3.   Success with Steam (1843–1856) 33

Chapter 4.   A Very Reputable Firm (1856–1867) 49

Chapter 5.   The Coming of the Compound and the End of an Era (1867–1878) 69

Chapter 6.   The Next Generation (1878–1899) 82

Chapter 7.   Under New Management (1899–1911) 96

Colour Plates 97

Chapter 8.   Conclusion 101

Penn Family Tree 2 103

Epilogue by Prudence Penn 104

Appendices 118

1   List of Penn Patents 118

2   Marine Engines made by the Firm 118

3   Lifespans of major Thameside Firms 122

4   Penn Almshouses 123

5   Places to visit and things to see 124

Sources 125

Notes and References 126

Index 128

Author's Preface

The story of the Penn's marine engineering firm took place through the 1800s. This was the century of the Royal Navy's worldwide dominance and its transformation from the wooden-walls of Trafalgar to the steam-driven, steel-built dreadnoughts of Jutland. It was the century during which steam was introduced into commercial shipping, starting with a few river and coastal vessels and ending with the demise of sailing ships. It was also a century of widespread industrialisation, urbanisation and of great political change. These transformations set the scene for the story of the firm and the family.

My interest in industrial history grew from my experiences in both UK and international, industrial management. During a thirty-six-year career I worked with companies operating in a wide range of economic and social situations. I experienced many of the changes which can occur in businesses and a wide range of contexts within which management decisions had to be taken. In my retirement I am a volunteer small business counsellor with the local Enterprise Agency: this experience has given me insight into owner-manager business.

I knew of the Penn's firm because my Hartree great-great grandfather was a partner. As I learned about the firm I decided to tell its story as an interesting example of Victorian industrial and business history.

In the course of my researches I met Prudence Penn, the widow of Sir Eric Penn who was a great-great grandson of the John Penn who founded the firm. She held the Penn family records and memorabilia and felt strongly that the story should be told and all the available material brought together in one volume. We decided that I should write the story of the three generations of the family involved in their engineering firm and that she, in an Epilogue, would write that of the three following generations in the very different field of Royal Service.

All monetary amounts are given in the numbers of the time. My rough guide is that at the start of the firm's story £1:0s:0d a week was a fair wage and at the end £2:0s:0d; inflation was gentle in the 1800s.

This is a history of a marine engineering firm and the family which owned and managed it. I could not avoid the use of some of the technical language that was used in steam marine engineering. I have included notes at the end of some chapters to describe, hopefully in layman's language, the terms I have used. The contemporary system of units – feet, inches, pounds and horsepower – is used.

I apologise to professional engineers for my unconventional use of the terms 'direct acting', 'connecting rod' and 'piston rod'. I hope my usage is clear from the diagrams and text.

Penn Family Tree I

(Those bold are mentioned in the text)

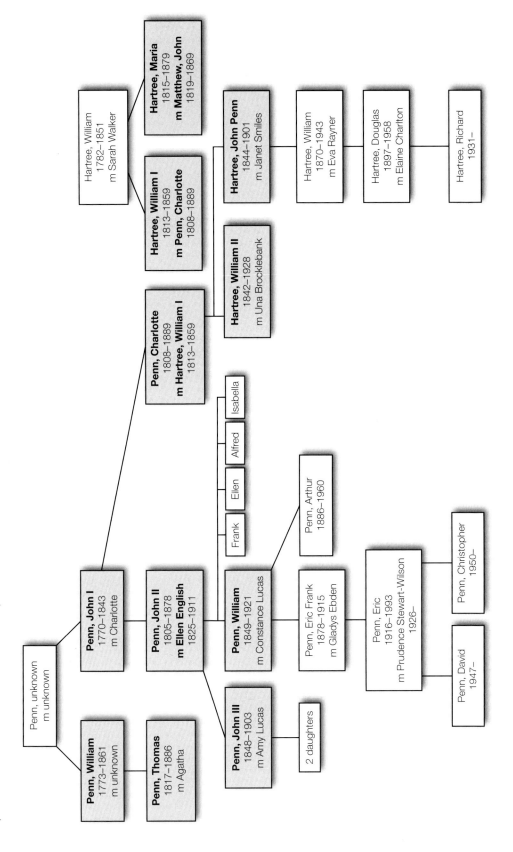

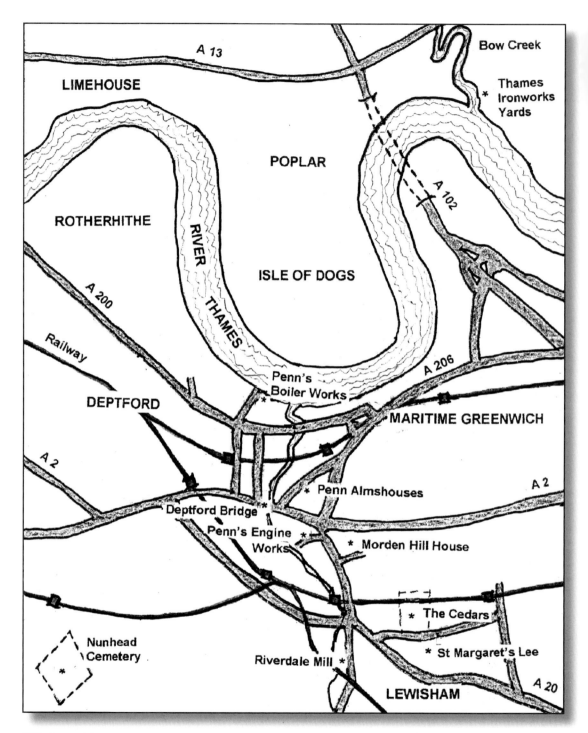

001 Area Map

1. Background and Early Years (1770–1825)

The firm was based in Greenwich. On the death of the second John Penn in 1878 *The Kentish Mercury and Greenwich Gazette* hailed him as 'Greenwich's Greatest Son'. He had been born and had his schooling and training in Greenwich. The firm was a major local employer and supplier to the Royal Navy and the reputation of its products had carried the name around the world. All this was achieved within the context of the times; that is, what is now the historical context starting in the eighteenth century.

Less than a mile from the works site is what is now known as Maritime Greenwich. The buildings of the old Royal Naval Hospital, later College, the National Maritime Museum and the Royal Observatory are its major attractions. In Wren's King William Court of the Hospital is the Painted Hall with its decoration, of 1708–25, by James Thornhill, showing Peace and Liberty triumphing over Tyranny and celebrating the perception of Britain as the leading seaborne commercial empire, protected by the power of the Royal Navy; a society encouraging enlightened thought, governed by a sovereign parliament and ruled by a Protestant constitutional monarch.[1] These features were seen to make Britain distinctly superior to the Catholic monarchies of continental Europe which were considered to be despotic and repressive.

During the next fifty years Britain, a largely rural society with the landed interests holding power both locally and in Parliament, underwent many changes. Agricultural improvements and land enclosures coupled with the growth of industrial manufacturing caused migrations of population and the beginnings of major urbanisation. The arrival of the Newcomen atmospheric steam engine as a source of power, largely for pumping, transformed the mining industry and made available greater supplies of coal and hence iron and other metals as raw materials for industry. The 1760s saw a burst of inventions and projects in the textile industry and, most important for this story, James Watt's steam engine with a separate condenser. There was also the canal-building boom which brought to national notice the engineers who designed and implemented large projects. The Seven Years War had seen Canada and other territories added to Britain's empire, further increasing the demands on the Royal Navy.

It was into this Britain that, in 1770, John Penn I (there will be II and III also) was born. There is no record of his birth but accepted fact is that it was near Taunton in Somerset. He was apprenticed as a millwright in Bridgwater and by 1791 was employed in Bristol as foreman of an important workshop. As a millwright he would have been knowledgeable about heavy wooden construction and familiar with the uses of wrought iron from the blacksmiths, of cast iron, of stone construction and possibly water control installations. He was known for his theoretical and practical knowledge of the form of the teeth of gear wheels to achieve smooth running and least wear.[2] At the time the mathematical understanding of this complex subject was imperfect and to achieve this reputation he must have had remarkable conceptual ability. Add to this his manual and managerial skills, plus the drive and ambition which took him to London in 1793, and there is a picture of a remarkable man.

Other events of these times which would have relevance to his future were, in 1780, the use of a steam engine to rotate a shaft which enabled steam power to be used to drive machinery. Then, in 1788, there was the demonstration of the use of a steam engine to drive a boat, on Dalswinton Lake in Dumfriesshire using an atmospheric engine built by William Symington; not the first steamboat but an early case of steam being used for locomotion.

A major historic event was the American War of Independence. At the time it may have been of more concern to the rulers of Britain, who were losing the colonies, than to the British people who, it seems, were able to maintain or easily re-establish their transatlantic contacts on a personal and business basis. The following comment by Lord Sheffield in 1786 is an interesting example of how some people were thinking at this early stage of industrialisation.

> If Mr Cort's very ingenious and meritorious improvements in the art of making and working iron, the steam engine of Boulton & Watt, and Lord Dundonald's discovery of making coke at half the present price, should all succeed, it is not asserting too much to say that the result will be more advantageous to Great Britain than the possession of the thirteen colonies; for it will give the complete command of the iron trade to this country, with its vast advantages to navigation.[3]

Lord Sheffield clearly agreed with the perception of Britain as the leading commercial empire supported by a dominant navy and welcomed the part industrialisation could play.

The French Revolution of 1789 set in motion a chain of events which dominate our view of the history of the next twenty-five years and which formed the context within which businesses in Britain worked. Those which were dependent on European trade suffered. Those serving the domestic market had confidence in the ability of Britain's naval power to defend the country from invasion and were able to grow. In these years Britain experienced social unrest and the government acted to curb some of the freedoms to hold meetings and to publish, which had characterised the earlier, more secure, enlightened age.

The Royal Navy held the body of organised knowledge related to ships, sail and the sea. Through the voyages of James Cook and others and the work of the Royal Observatory at Greenwich it was establishing itself as the world's leading ocean surveyor and cartographer. The provisioning and supply of the Navy was a vast undertaking and the naval dockyards were quick to adopt industrial methods. The Navy's engineering and industrial knowledge was largely held by civilians, not by the ranking officers for whom fine seamanship was the key to success.

A millwright's training like that of John Penn I provided the basic experience for many famous engineers of the times; others came from backgrounds in carpentry and smithy work. There was no profession of engineer. Men who took on major projects, such as Brindley, Telford, and Smeaton, became known as engineers largely from their involvement in what we now call civil engineering projects – drainage, dockyards and canals. The term mechanic was used for those whose main work was with machinery. There was no opportunity for theoretical training of engineers and mechanics; this is hardly surprising as there was little scientifically based theory to teach. In continental Europe there was a tradition of training in military engineering which had a strong civil engineering bias related to the construction of fortifications. Britain had no standing army, her defence was the sea and the country saw little public need for that kind of engineering skill.

The size of London and the great variety of goods and facilities required to sustain and entertain its population led to the presence of many small workshops employing skilled men in a wide variety of trades. Like many others John Penn I came to London both to learn and to find opportunities. Quite a few returned home and made their businesses there, but many stayed. Engineers came because London was the centre for major civil projects, many needing parliamentary approval. The mechanics came for the experience and the opportunities.[4] One of the first was Joseph Brahmah, a joiner and cabinetmaker from Yorkshire who set up shop in Denmark Street, St Giles, moving in 1784 to Piccadilly and in 1806 to Pimlico, where by 1814 he employed 110 men, which was a very large shop at that time. His work attracted other exceptional men such as Henry Maudslay from the Royal Arsenal at Woolwich in 1790 and Joseph Clement, formerly of Westmorland, Glasgow and Aberdeen, in 1813. In 1797 Maudslay left Bramah to set up on his own because he was refused a rise in pay to above thirty shillings a week. His first workshop was off Oxford Street and he moved to near Cavendish Square in1802. All these workshop premises were in what we now know as the West End.

Most of the engineers who appear later in the story came to London during these years. Maudslay was given the contract to build the machines which industrialised the manufacture of the pulley blocks which were needed in large numbers for the Navy's square-rigged sailing ships. His increasing workload necessitated a move to larger premises and in 1810 he moved away from London, to Lambeth. He went on to become the father of the machine tool industry through the development of machine tools and practices which were vital for consistent accuracy of manufacture. His Lambeth-based engineering business became the national leader for high-quality engineering and the main training ground for those who went on to become the finest mechanical engineers of the mid-1800s; Joseph Whitworth [5] and Joseph Clement [6] for example.

Whitworth had come to London from Manchester and returned there to set up his own business. Clement established his own business in London and was well known to John Penn II. Although not trained by Maudslay, John Penn I was accepted as a member of this community of skilled mechanics. It was the pattern for ambitious, skilled men to take a job in a reputable workshop, gain knowledge and experience, accumulate some capital by saving from their wages and then start their own business. This route to entrepreneurship required more than technical skills. It needed creativity, a clear vision of the goal, persistent application, determination and business judgement. There would have been many who tried and of whom there is no record. Success required exceptional men.

Nothing is known of John Penn I's first six years in and around London but it is reasonable to suppose that he followed the usual pattern and worked for several small mechanics and millwrights both in their shops and out on contracts. In 1799 he established an agricultural and general engineering business in Greenwich.[7] Greenwich was an interesting choice of location as it was then quite a distance from the city and from the opportunities which most other mechanics favoured. He may have chosen Greenwich because of a good local contract – a 1799 customer was Goodhow and Gordon & Co, distillers. His early lines of business were more rural than urban: agricultural implements and machinery, millwork and forcing houses – or greenhouses. The business started on a site, rented from the Holwell charity, at the junction of Blackheath and Lewisham Roads with its entrance off what is now John Penn [101, p12], previously Bath, Street [001, Area Map, p8]. No doubt this location was chosen because it was affordable and convenient for the business at the time. The firm remained there throughout its life despite the great changes which occurred in the nature of its business. It is now occupied by a DIY store and a pet supplies outlet

(Appendix 5, p123). The only extant company record gives the names of customers who had accounts in the first decade. It includes the Earl of Dartmouth (Lord of the Manor of Lewisham, a large local landowner), a Mr Wills at Beverly Mills, and Kent Water Works, which had, and still has, a plant located just below Penn's works.

101 Greenwich street sign

It was through the activities of Bramah, Maudslay, Penn and many others less known that the mechanical engineering industry came into being during John Penn I's lifetime. In 1805, together with the other engineers Bryan Donkin, John Rennie and John Hall, John Penn I started a Millwrights' society.[8] Some such societies were formed by millwrights who wished to protect their jobs by limiting recruitment to locally qualified men. The one founded by Penn and others was, as an employers' association, trying to keep opportunities open. When William Fairbairn first came from the North-East to London he was refused a job on Rennie's London Bridge project because his qualifications were not recognised. He obtained work elsewhere where the millwrights were not so particular. In 1812 he worked for Penn for a couple of months, leaving when orders fell off. He was one of several who subsequently went to Manchester to start up his own business.

The business of the mechanical engineers was different from that of the civil engineers. The civil engineer conceived, sold and developed designs for structures and, although he would supervise the construction, it was the contractor who had the responsibility for its completion. The mechanical engineer sold and designed his machines and was usually directly responsible for their manufacture and all the facilities and men required. Our heritage finds it easier to remember the civil engineer than the mechanical because of the survival of many very visible, grand structures compared to the few remarkable machines now in museum collections. The industrial revolution would not have been possible without the machines made by the machine tools which these mechanics created.

The shipbuilding industry, with which the firm became closely associated, had a long and very different history in London. It was a highly skilled, craft industry which could be practised on both small and large scales. Ships were built of wood by shipwrights and carpenters supported by sailmakers, ropemakers, caulkers, blacksmiths and others. London, the largest port in the country, had been the major centre for both naval and merchant shipbuilding for centuries. The two Royal Dockyards at Deptford and Woolwich were large industrial establishments. The private shipyards were smaller, some very small, but there were many of them. All were below London Bridge and the Tower. On the north bank they were at Wapping, Shadwell and Limehouse, and on the south bank almost continuous round the Rotherhithe bend to Deptford. Thames-built ships had a very good reputation; 'river-built' and 'Blackwall fashion' were well-known terms for high quality.

During these early years John Penn I's concentration on the business would have been intense. Like any start-up business his first objective must have been to achieve survival, the next to build the customer base to achieve security and then to accumulate capital for further investment and growth. In those times, as now, an almost obsessive attention to work was required to win through.

John Penn I must have done well. Some time in the first five years of the business he changed his life in another way. He married, at an age between 30 and 35, and started a family. There is no record of his marriage. There is no record of the birth of his son John Penn II in 1805, but the baptism of his daughter Charlotte, at St Alphage's, Greenwich, in 1808 is recorded with her mother's name given as Charlotte. The family home was near the corner of Lewisham and Blackheath Roads, probably number 10 Lewisham Road backing on to the works site [420, Works Layout, Ch 4, p68].

The battle of Trafalgar, in 1805, ended the threat of a Napoleonic invasion and was the ultimate demonstration of Britain's naval power under sail, although no one realised that at the time. About this time a lesser, but for the firm's future business more important, event took place far away when, in 1808, the world's first commercial steamboat service started on the Hudson River between New York and Albany with Robert Fulton's *Clermont*. This was followed soon after by services on the Clyde and between Gourock and Belfast. The first steamboat appeared on the Thames in 1813. These were the first commercial uses of steam as a source of power for moving people and goods. It is interesting to note that these marine steam developments took place well before the opening of the first commercial steam railways – the Stockton and Darlington in 1825 and the Liverpool and Manchester in 1830. Boats did not need a track to be built, which made things much simpler, and they could make use of heavier, more cumbersome engines than railway locomotives. The limitations on the use of steam power for boats quickly became obvious. A steam engine needed to be supplied with fuel, wood or coal, and fresh, not sea, water, to be converted into steam. Seawater was not suitable because of the formation of scale in the boiler. The large continental rivers of North America and Europe provided ideal conditions. The smaller rivers and canals of Britain were not so suitable for the large-scale use of steam power. Estuary or coastal services where fuel and fresh water could be carried for the whole journey became the main starting point for marine steam in Britain. In all these the engine provided the power to drive paddles. Sternwheelers became common on the large continental rivers – think of *Showboat* – whereas sidewheelers were used in British waters, like the *Waverley* pleasure steamers. Monet's *The Thames below Westminster*, although of much later date, shows several sidewheelers.

The weight and size of the engine and boiler and of the fuel added to the weight of the vessel and so reduced the load-carrying capacity. The commercial consequence was that steam was uncompetitive against sail for cargo vessels but worthwhile for passenger and mail ships which could charge higher prices for faster, less weather-dependent and hence more reliable, steam services. This situation continued for a long time. To extend their range in the open sea and to provide an alternative motive force in case of engine breakdown, the early steam sea-going vessels always had sails.

Penn's customer account list grew and included Stratford Mills in 1812; Fairbairn had worked there. The firm's range of products grew with the addition of bakery machinery, gunpowder mills and other industrial products. An important development in the mid-1810s was the introduction of cast-iron framing in place of wood for support structures in millwork and for the frames of machine tools. The millwrights' restrictive practices may have inspired this but it also gave more rigid, robust, longer-life machinery. He also, along with most mechanics' works, began to introduce self-acting machinery; the very beginnings of putting the skill in the machine rather than in the man. Product quality was more reliable and did not require such a high level of operator skill. It would have been another response to restrictive practices as well as a step in the drive for quality and consistency. John Penn I was on close terms with William and Thomas Howard who ran the King and Queen Ironworks in Rotherhithe.[9] This firm had a high reputation for wrought- and cast-iron products. The Howards could well have helped him in his use of cast iron for structures and supplied wrought iron to the firm. It would be reasonable to assume that John Penn installed a cupola furnace and iron foundry for making his own castings at about this time. This would have been a significant investment. The handling of basic raw materials and of molten iron, plus the making of wooden patterns, would have brought about a major change in the scale of activities at the works.

The first steam packet service on the Thames was in 1815 with the Clyde-built *Margery* and *Thames*. By 1817 there had been a number of accidents caused by exploding boilers on ships and involving stationary engines on land. These led to a scheme of registration for boilers which was the early forerunner of the inspection and certification of pressure vessel codes today. Explosions and fires on ships were particularly dangerous so that, for safety reasons, marine boilers were oper-ated at much lower pressures than boilers on land and hence were less efficient, which affected steam's competitiveness with sail.

The year 1815 saw the end of the long period of war and the start of a long period of peace. Some other, at the time unrelated events, were the births of William Hartree in 1813 in Rotherhithe – his father had come from Somerset and married in Southwark in 1807 – of Thomas Penn in 1817, the son of John Penn I's younger brother William; and of John Matthew in 1819 in Green-wich.[10] All three went on to have careers in the firm. William Hartree married Charlotte Penn.

In 1818 John Penn II entered his apprenticeship at his father's works. He was then thirteen and since the age of six had been at a school run by a Mr Mellor located in a large house in The Pits off the Lewisham Road.[11] The work of the firm was to make machines out of metal parts. Parts started as rough shapes produced by casting – pouring molten metal into a shaped mould – or by forging – hammering hot metal on an anvil. The cast or forged pieces were hand-cut and shaped with chisels, files and scrapers to the dimensions required. Starting with the discipline of tidiness, the use of these tools, together with accurate measurement and marking out, were the basic skills John Penn II learned. He would also have learned how to use the lathe and the drill, and how to maintain the cutting tools. He was a keen and hard-working pupil. His father would have made sure he was guided by the best workers in the firm.

The only machine tools of the times were the lathe, the boring machine and the drill, with the smaller ones powered by the operator using a treadle. Larger machines could be powered by tread-mill, horse gin, wind or water mill. The planing machine, to make flat surfaces, was introduced by Clement in the 1820s. Most of the basic machine tool designs were developed later in the 1800s. It was usual for mechanics' shops to make machine tools to their own designs to meet their spe-cial needs, and Penn's did this quite extensively. The basic hand-tool skills with file and scraper remained essential in engineering shops throughout the century and beyond.

At this time William Cubitt, a Suffolk-based millwright and engineer, had introduced the idea of large treadmills as a way to make use of prison labour by having the prisoners mill flour for their own consumption and for sale. It became a means of prison discipline: the exercising prisoners could be readily supervised. Usually the tread had the width for ten men. As well as climbing it they walked along it and had a break after reaching the end and before starting again. Ideally, with twelve men on a ten-man mill, one fifth of their time would have been on break. A number of millwright firms acted as contractors to build treadmills to Cubitt's designs. Penn is known to have built one at Brixton prison.

In the years after Waterloo, economic and social change continued to disrupt society. Further land enclosures, agricultural improvements and mechanisation led to distress and protest in the shires, often expressed by the crowd through deliberate rick-burning and machine breakage. Rule by the magistrate, usually the local squire or parson, backed by the militia, held this at manageable levels. In the urban areas where the influx of people kept wages low, protest could rise up over matters as varied as the price of bread and the drive for parliamentary reform. The 1819 incident at St Peter's Fields in Manchester when the yeomanry, called by the magistrate, charged the crowd of some sixty thousand gathered to listen to a reformist speaker and caused eleven deaths, became known as the Peterloo Massacre. Fear of the mob was very real as there was no standing police force to maintain law and order. Business opportunities grew despite this social background, but it is reasonable to assume that it influenced John Penn I's political views and future action.

It was in 1819 that the Institution of Civil Engineers had been founded. Although founded for engineers rather than mechanics it was a professional and learned society which attracted members from a range of engineering interests.

In 1820 there were forty steamers on the Clyde and twenty on the Thames. A paddle steamer boom had started. The Admiralty had watched these developments and realised that the delays to sailing ships entering or leaving harbour due to unfavourable wind and tidal currents could be eliminated by the use of steam-powered tugs. The paddle tug *Monkey*, the first steam vessel in the Navy, came into service in this year. She was followed by others. These first naval steam vessels were not given the HMS title and their crews were not incorporated into the Navy. They were the start of the long process of the Navy's transition from sail to steam. Spread over a hundred years the transition involved major changes in ship design, materials, armament and auxiliary equipment and also in the command structure on board and in the social attitudes of executive officers. Seventy years later John Penn III would become involved in the final chapters of this story.

In 1822, aged 17, John Penn II built a small steam engine to provide power in the works. This would have been a good exercise of his skills. Matthew Boulton's 1774 claim that 'I sell here, Sir, what all the world desires to have – Power'[12] still rang true and the manufacture of steam engines was the ambition of many young engineers. He followed this with a larger engine which was still in use at the works over sixty years later. In 1822 the firm undertook the repair of the engine of the vessel *Nero* and in 1824 made a new boiler for her. These two jobs were the firm's first recorded venture into marine engineering, which was not then recognised as a specialised field of engineering.

Under the leadership of Bramah, Rennie, Maudslay and Penn a mechanical engineering industry grew up in London with, in 1825, five or six shops – including those four – employing over forty men each, and four or five hundred shops with fewer than ten each.[13] In this period London had a major role in the development of mechanical engineering in Britain.[14] The large number of workshops, the concentration of skills and the ever-growing business opportunities of the capital created the conditions for it to flourish. John Penn I's firm was an important part of the development of the industry.

Note on steam engines

Early steam engines were used for pumping water out of mines or land drainage. The pumps lifted water up a tube. A long rod went up and down in the tube to raise and lower the pump's piston. This rod was attached to one end of a rocking beam. The piston rod of the engine was attached to the other end of the beam and the engine's piston went up and down in a cylinder. This type of engine is known as a beam engine. The up stroke for the engine was driven by the falling weight of the pump rods and piston. As the engine piston was raised in the cylinder steam was introduced below the piston from a boiler so that at the top of the stroke the cylinder was full of steam. Then cold water was injected into the cylinder, the steam condensed to water, a vacuum was created and the pressure of the atmosphere on the top of the piston pushed it down, so raising the pump rod and pumping water from the mine. Because the vacuum was not perfect the pressure on the piston was always less the 15 pounds per square inch (psi) of the atmosphere. This was known as an atmospheric engine.

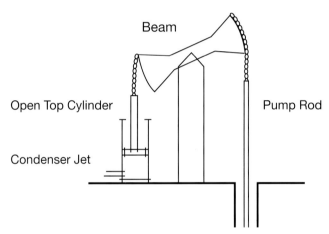

Beam

Open Top Cylinder

Pump Rod

Condenser Jet

102 Atmospheric Pumping Engine, diagram

James Watt had realised that this was a very inefficient way of using steam. The engine cylinder was always cool as the steam was fed into it from the boiler. Consequently much of the steam condensed on entry into the cylinder. Thus a lot more steam was needed than would be required if the cylinder were to be kept hot. He invented the separate condenser so that the cylinder was not cooled by the condensation of the steam. The condenser was connected to the cylinder by a pipe with a valve. The valve was opened when the piston was at the top of its stroke; steam flowed into the condenser and was condensed there. Atmospheric pressure on top of the piston pushed it down as in the atmospheric engine and the valve was closed when the piston reached the bottom. Steam was again introduced as the piston rose and the cycle repeated. He also realised that if the top of the cylinder was closed, with a seal around the piston rod, steam from the boiler could be introduced into the top of the cylinder to push the piston down with more than atmospheric pressure and that this would give even greater power. He further realised that, with appropriate pipes and valves, both up and down strokes could be powered by steam and so give smoother and greater power. This was the double-acting engine.

There were many difficulties in making engines reliable and efficient: practical difficulties with the accurate machining of the parts; materials difficulties with bearings, with the packings for piston rings, piston rod glands, and with the materials for and manufacture of the boilers. In operation there were difficulties with the performance of lubricants for the rotating and sliding metal-to-metal bearings, for the hot and wet piston rings and piston rod glands and so on.

At first engines were only providing up and down power. It was obvious that rotary power was needed to operate machinery. This was done by having the pump rod become the connecting rod to a crank which was attached to a rotating shaft. This had its own set of practical difficulties which were gradually overcome. To achieve smooth power it was realised that a heavy rotating flywheel was needed and that two single-acting cylinders applied to cranks on opposite sides of the shaft, like bicycle pedals, were better than one; for double-acting engines the cranks were at right angles.

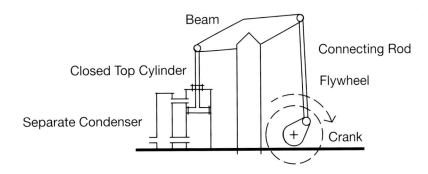

103 'Watt' Rotating Engine, diagram

The double-acting, separate condenser, beam engine driving a crank became the basis for the wider industrial exploitation of steam power. Initially these were all built with the cylinder vertical, which meant that the weight of the piston was not bearing on the piston ring or packing or on the cylinder wall.

The height of the normal beam engine made it rather unsuitable for use in steam paddle ships. Designs were developed with the beams at the side of the cylinders, known as side-lever engines. [104, p18]

Early boilers were like kettles: a dome above a firebox. These were followed by cylindrical boilers with the firebox at one end and the hot gases from the fire passing under and around the cylinder before going up the funnel. In the early boilers steam pressures were between 5 and 15 psi. With steam on one side of the piston and the partial vacuum on the other the maximum pressure on the piston during the stroke could be around 20 psi. The average over the whole stroke was lower.

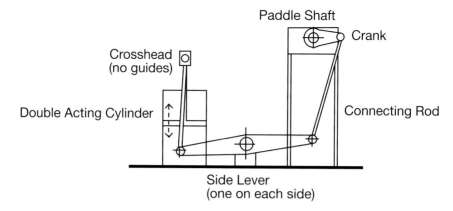

104 Side-Lever Engine for Paddle Steamer, diagram

In these boilers vaporisation of the water to steam takes place submerged at the interface of the water with the hot surface, like the bubbles forming at the bottom of a pan. During heating the hot water rises from the hot surface and before vaporisation can start all the water in the boiler, or pan, must be heated to boiling point. Then the water must receive the latent heat necessary for vaporisation. One consequence of this is that it takes a long time to get the engine started from cold and another is that there is a lot of scalding water in the boiler which could create havoc if the boiler bursts.

The condenser was another large unit. It had to be able to receive the steam from the cylinder quickly and to condense it. An air pump emptied the condenser of the air which leaked in and of the water from the condensing steam. In the early condensers a jet of cold water was squirted in to cause cooling and condensation; this followed the earlier practice of squirting cold water into the cylinder and hence these were known as jet condensers. This was practical where there was a copious supply of fresh water, as on land, lake or river. But salt seawater changed the situation. Salt water was bad for the boilers and engine so a system of boiler, engine and condenser which could operate with as little loss of fresh water as possible was needed for marine engines. An approach was to cool the outside of the condenser with seawater, or to have cooled tubes running through the condenser. Condensation then took place on the cold surfaces of the condenser or tubes, not in contact with the salt water; hence these were known as surface condensers. Successful surface condenser designs needed development of methods to make the tubes, of types of brass to make then from and of methods to fix the tubes in the end plates.

A reader who would like an introduction to marine engineering could use one of the books listed in the Sources. Any local library should be able to obtain it.

2. INTO STEAM (1825–1843)

In the early 1800s Steam Navigation was the name given to the business of companies which operated steamboats. It was a new field of business activity based on a new technology. There was almost no operating experience to guide the new operator regarding likely operating costs, the shipbuilder regarding the best type of vessel for the task or the engine builder regarding the specification and design of the engines. The little knowledge that existed was not published so personal contacts, and those not with possible competitors, were the only way to learn anything useful. All this made any new venture a risky undertaking for all involved.

Ipswich had a long history in shipbuilding to a high standard. In 1824 a group of local businessmen promoted the Ipswich Steam Navigation Company, offering twice-weekly sailings for passengers and goods between Ipswich and London.[1] William Cubitt, of the treadmills mentioned in Chapter 1, acted as Company Secretary and Engineer. The Company was founded on 1 January 1825 with an initial capital of £20,000. Soon a contract was placed with George Bayley and John Ridley's yard in Ipswich to build two vessels and in April John Penn I entered into a contract to provide the drive systems – boilers, engines and paddle wheels – for the two steamers, one pair of engines for each. The Company was a new venture and this was probably Penn's first contract for marine engines and the first for Bayley and Ridley for steam vessels. John Penn I agreed to supply and fit the two complete systems for £5,000. The agreement was made in April and delivery to Ipswich was to be in July and August, which left about ten weeks to complete design and manufacture and to deliver the first pair to Ipswich, allowing a further month for the second pair. The engines were to be 'put to work' within five weeks of delivery. The work was to be of the highest quality and had to be approved by William Cubitt. It is reasonable to assume that the Company hoped to start the London service in September that year.

The engines were twin-cylinder, side-lever engines with boilers working at 4 psi which was normal for the times. The business opportunity for steam navigation was seen as the provision of a reliable service rather than one at the mercy of the wind and weather, as were sailing vessels. Machinery reliability, rather than fuel efficiency, was seen as the key to success. The ships were called *Ipswich* and *Suffolk*.

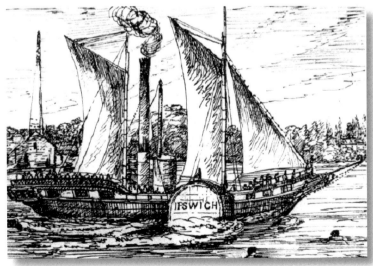

201
Ipswich,
1825

The contract provided for £1,500 to be paid to Penn before delivery, treated as a loan at 5 per cent. A further £500 would be paid on the delivery and then again on the 'putting to work' of each pair of engines. There was a £10 per week penalty clause for late delivery of the engines if the vessels were ready. The £1,500 balance was to be paid three months after completion, which was planned to be by the end of 1825. John Penn I also bound himself to £2,500,

> ...by way of special and liquidated damages on the non-performance or other non-observance of any matter of thing in the contract except those already covered together with the cost of any suit.

This was an ambitious job and a tight contract, and the price would have reflected that. Most writings about John Penn II give the impression that this was his project. He may well have made a significant design contribution but, as the date was before his twenty-first birthday, it must have been his father's contract.

The whole project did not go according to plan or contract. *Ipswich* was not launched until September 1825, two months late, and was then towed to Greenwich for the engines to be installed. *Suffolk* followed two months later, three months late, with *Ipswich* towing her to Greenwich for the installation of the engines. These delays must have given difficulties with the application of the contract terms. The first commercial sailing was by *Ipswich* in April 1826. *Suffolk* entered the service in September and twice-weekly sailings were then established until the end of October, when the service was suspended for the winter 'as is general practice for Steam Vessels'.

That winter some of the bankers involved in the Company also promoted a venture using sailing vessels to carry cargo at lower cost. In 1827 the steamer fares were increased and only *Suffolk* went into service, and she again stopped for the winter. In March 1828 both vessels were laid up and were eventually sold in 1829 for the sum of £1,800 for the two. The Company had not paid Bayley and Ridley or John Penn I in full for the work they had done. This default contributed to the dissolution of the Bayley and Ridley partnership. The dispute with John Penn I went to arbitration at the time of the collapse of the Company in 1831, six years after the contract. The Company no longer existed so John Penn made his claim for £3,000 against the members of the original Management Committee. Bryan Donkin of Kent, known to John Penn I, and Robert Hawthorn of Newcastle, presumably known to the members of the Committee, were named as arbitrators. They could call in other specialists and Joshua Field, later of Maudslay, Son & Field, joined them and the records are thanks to him. They include a copy of the oath which John Penn I signed as witness in the dispute, confirming that it was his contract. The arbitrators awarded John Penn £1,081:17s, and his costs. The expenses of arbitration, £181:17s, were shared. Penn would no doubt still have felt himself considerably out of pocket. This had proved to be a risky and expensive venture for all parties and not a good entry into marine engineering for the firm. There was an order for the side-lever engines of a small naval vessel named *Medea*, built in the Woolwich dockyard in 1833, but after it the firm had no marine orders for a few years.

Ipswich and *Suffolk* were not the only steam navigation business failure. Many steamship operators were rather surprised when they came to realise the high running and maintenance costs of steamers, but despite these setbacks the promotion of steam navigation continued. The London to Margate pleasure steamer service became very popular, with 50,000 people a year making the journey by 1825. Their tall funnels can be seen in Turner's 1826/8 watercolour *Margate*. Competition for passengers led to a desire for faster vessels. By the 1830s Thomas Ditchburn of Fletcher and Fearnall's Limehouse yard had realised that to achieve speed the paddle boats required a different hull design than that used for sailing ships. The hull needed to be longer and narrower, with the paddle wheels placed so that the bow wave would not affect the working of the paddles. Built to this design his vessels had a competitive advantage.

An entirely different project came to the firm through Jacob Perkins, an American inventor who had settled in London.[2] He arrived in 1819 and set up in business in Fleet Street. He was busy with several ideas, one of which was the Steam Gun. This would use high-pressure steam to propel the shot from the gun barrel. His first trials were in 1824. Towards the end of the year the neighbours' complaints about the noise of his trials caused him to move to Albany Street on the edge of Regent's Park. On 6 December 1825 there was a demonstration witnessed by the Duke of Wellington. The gun performed magnificently, at 900 psi steam pressure. The Duke is reported to have said, 'Wonderful, wonderful, damned wonderful'. However, nothing came of it because the gun and boiler were too heavy to be transported in military field operations and the time, of over half an hour, to raise steam from cold was unacceptable for field artillery. John Penn II is reported by John Bourne[3] as saying that he had been employed by Jacob Perkins, presumably after completion of his apprenticeship, and was present at that trial although *The Times* report does not mention him. The Duke is said to have been more impressed by John Penn II than the gun and to have spoken well of him afterwards. This cannot be confirmed, but if true it could well have helped Penn in his future relations with government departments. The experience gave him an opportunity to expand his knowledge of engineering.

In 1825 John Penn II became an Associate Member of the Institution of Civil Engineers. He was proposed by Robert Sibley, who is recorded as a Surveyor with an address in Great Ormond Street, London. This once again shows that John Penn II was making contacts beyond his Greenwich roots.

After being turned down by the British government Jacob Perkins took the Steam Gun to France. The French government ordered a larger gun to be built and the contract went to John Penn I's firm. The only existing company records concern this project. Trials in 1827 near the Greenwich site were witnessed by the Prince de Polignac, who became chief minister to Charles X. In 1828 a price of £1,135:14s:4½d was charged for the supply of one tested gun; this included £1:0s:0d for damage to a neighbour's garden during the tests. A duplicate was supplied for £1,222:18s:4½d.[4] Following the shipment of the first gun to France in May 1828 John Penn II went to Paris to work on it and stayed until the trials, which were held at the Chateau de Vincennes in October. In the end the French did not support the project. The oral history of the Penn family is that during this time John Penn II formed a romantic liaison in Paris which led to a child or children and to his maintaining a household in Paris for some while. Bearing in mind that he was an attractive, energetic young man on his own in Paris this is quite believable but it is not validated.

Another of Perkins's schemes was his patent Uniflow steam engine for marine applications. His single-acting compound design was very novel, containing several unproven ideas in both boiler and engine design including working at very high, over 1,000 psi, steam pressures. A letter which Perkins wrote in March 1827 tells that he had granted a licence to John Penn to build the engine. He had earlier approached the Russian navy about his engine and they had asked the British Admiralty for comments. This shows that he must have been a very persistent salesman. Despite all its novelties the idea was to sell the engine with performance guarantees. He mentions making a contract with John Penn for the manufacture of these engines and says Penn employed three hundred men at his works in Greenwich – a number which may well have been Perkins's fancy rather than fact; it was the number of employees at Greenwich twenty-five years later. The whole idea came to nothing, which is not at all surprising considering the risks it entailed. Whether the licence deal was just Perkins's wishful thinking or whether he might have had an encouraging response from John Penn II, possibly influenced by Perkins's enthusiasm, which was sensibly squashed by John Penn I, will never be known; Penn's attitude would have been strongly influenced by the *Ipswich* and *Suffolk* episode.

Perkins got into financial trouble shortly after this. Penn's accounts record that work on an engine for Perkins was billed in 1831–2 and not fully paid for. There was also a quotation to Perkins for a steam engine and for consultancy in 1839; John Penn II asked for a fee of £7:10s:0d a week plus expenses. Perkins was an inventor with a fertile mind but, in these steam applications, a love for way-out ideas and little appreciation of the practical needs of the operator. He appears to have been a man who would not take 'no' for an answer, which probably explains the length of the relationship. All this would have been a valuable learning experience for John Penn II. His own innovations were, in contrast, all based on a careful assessment of the user's needs and on the application of incremental changes to proven technologies.

Following his visit to France, John Penn II visited many engineers and workshops in England, Scotland, Belgium, Holland, Germany, Switzerland, Italy and France to study practices and learn all he could of their methods.[5] This reads like an engineer's Grand Tour and it probably was. It is certain that he would have had his father's encouragement and support. John Penn I's commitment to his son's training shows that he had a vision for the firm beyond what he could achieve himself. It was probably following the completion of these visits that the father took the son into partnership and the firm became known as John Penn & Son.

An, at the time unrelated, event of 1828 was William Hartree's start of his apprenticeship with a stationer in the City. The stationer was a near neighbour in Rotherhithe Street. It is hard to imagine how this trained him for a future as a partner in an engineering firm, but it must be remembered that specialisation and professional titles had less significance in those times. In 1830 Thomas Penn, nephew of John Penn I, started his apprenticeship in the firm.

Since the Napoleonic wars there had been a big cut in the budget for the Navy. Manning levels had been severely reduced and many ships put into reserve. The underlying policy remained that of maintaining a fleet larger than that of any likely foe. It was a fleet which also had to be able to maintain a worldwide reach and its ships had to be able to spend long periods at sea, which put a premium on reliability. These conditions were not conducive to experimentation but it was realised that a policy for steam must be formed.

A sensible approach to the technical development within the budget restraints was to use the mail packets being built for the Post Office as prototype vessels. Success would benefit the Post Office and serve the Navy. Two went into service in 1821 and demonstrated their superiority over the commercial packet service. In 1822 a purpose-designed steam tug, *Comet*, was built at Deptford. Her usefulness was soon apparent and when she towed a dredger in open sea from Woolwich to Portsmouth the concept of a tug took on new meaning. She was followed by a larger vessel,

Lightning, launched in 1823 which in 1824 went, accompanied by a sail collier and towed by a ship-of-the-line for most of the open sea journey, with a squadron which was to put an end to piracy from Algiers.

There was no such easy solution to the organisational and social issues in the Navy caused by the introduction of steam. In 1828 the commanding officers of naval steamers were civilians or naval half-pay masters or mates re-employed as civilians. Neither the ships nor the crews were commissioned. The Navy had an acute problem with the place of engineers in the command structure of a commissioned ship. Command was seen as the job of commissioned military, or executive, officers. Commissioned officers were appointed by patronage and were customarily the sons of country gentlemen and the like. Then there were the Masters who managed the ship and the Pursers, Surgeons and Chaplains who were Warrant Officers of wardroom rank. They all came from totally different social backgrounds from those of the men who knew about the operation and maintenance of steam engines – men who got their hands dirty. They could not believe that an engineer could behave properly at the wardroom table, nor how he could know how to manage men, as he came from a class which had not been 'born to lead'; rather, they would think, from a class 'born to serve'. The consequence of this was that the engineers messed separately, usually were allowed cabins, but were regarded as little more than ratings. Bearing in mind the engineer's responsibility for major equipment which was vital to the vessel's performance, of which the executive officers had little or no understanding, plus their responsibility for a substantial proportion of the total crew – stokers, boiler men and engine-room hands – this was not a sustainable situation.

In 1830 Joshua Field wrote a letter to the Comptroller of the Navy in which he outlined the problems and difficulties that were being caused by the Navy's attitude towards its engineers and compared it very unfavourably with the merchant service.[6] He pointed out that it led to real difficulties in recruiting and retaining engineering personnel; also that pay was better in the merchant service and, with lighter discipline, conditions were more amenable.

In 1827 there were over two hundred steamships registered under the Merchant Shipping Acts. Services included Holyhead to Dublin and even Dublin to Bordeaux as well as cross-Channel. Ten years later the number had risen to over six hundred and routes were saturated. The capital costs were much higher than for sail, as also were the operating costs. The high cost of maintenance of the older engines was becoming apparent. The firm of John Penn, after the *Ipswich* and *Suffolk* experience, had not made much of an inroad into this business and the Navy was confining its engine orders to Boulton & Watt and Maudslay, Son & Field – as Maudslay's business was called after 1831.

The Navy was also developing secure bases for the supply of all the needs of the fleet and its men. Industrial-scale victualling yards were built at the Royal Dockyards of Plymouth, Portsmouth and Deptford. The sea-biscuit – a water biscuit – was a basic item in the sailors' rations. A common feature of these yards was a mechanised biscuit bakery. The Deptford bakery was opened in 1833.[7] John Rennie and his brother had built the first of these in Plymouth, a second was built in Portsmouth modelled on their work and the third was at Deptford. Rennie, in his *Autobiography*, claims that the work on all three was done by he and his brother. This was not the case in Portsmouth and, if the reports on Penn are accepted, it was not the case at Deptford either. It is most likely that Penn's firm supplied the machinery which was made to designs similar to those which John Rennie had used in Plymouth and had been installed in Portsmouth.[8] It would have been a big contract for the firm and, after the trouble with *Ipswich* and *Suffolk*, a welcome boost to the business.

Much else was happening in Britain other than the development of ships and marine engineering. The Bristol riots of 1831 were a sharp reminder of the power of an angry mob. The pressure for social and political change was strong and the aristocratic, land-based ruling majority realised that change was inevitable. Parliamentary reform had been the subject of a prolonged public and parliamentary debate but to no effect. William Cobbett, journalist, pamphleteer and MP, was one of the most persistent and active advocates of reform. Eventually, in 1832, the first Reform Bill was passed by parliament. The Bill met some of the demands of the reformers including an end to the Rotten Boroughs, which had very small populations but more members than the new urban areas, and the creation of more members for the industrial urban areas, but omitted the demands for a broader franchise and for election by ballot rather than public show of hands.

John Penn I has been described as 'a keen politician and a friend of William Cobbett.'[9] The passing of the Reform Bill provided him with an opportunity to become active. He became the reformist candidate for the representation of Greenwich in the December 1832 parliamentary election. It is interesting to note that this first Penn venture into politics is not mentioned in any of the writings about John Penn II, which are the source of most of the information about his father.

The Times gave a report on the Greenwich election.[10] The candidates and their friends appeared at the hustings at nine o'clock, and the reception given to Captain Dundas and Mr Barnard, the sitting members, was most flattering. That given to Messrs Angerstein, Hammond and Penn was of mixed character. The candidates were proposed – Mr Penn by Mr Poule of the Political Union, a reform group, and Mr Lambert. The report states:

> In his speech Mr Penn strongly condemned the present system of taxation, and declared that to save the country from ultimate convulsion it was necessary to attack it with a vigorous hand. They should not listen to any talk about the necessity of substituting one tax for another. The system must be changed, and the amount diminished. Reform was not complete; 2,000 or 3,000 persons in the borough were excluded from the franchise. The want of a ballot was also felt. (Murmurs) Attacks the most unwarrantable had been made ('No, no') on the freedom of election in Greenwich ('Name, name'). All the learned and philosophical societies voted by ballot. The people should return none but friends of the people, but he thought they did not go far enough for improvement. (Confusion.) He was the enemy of sinecures, nor would he waste seven years discussing the propriety of a pension before it was cut off. The removal of taxes was the only mode of checking extravagant profusion. He would not amuse them with generalities: he would vote for specific measures – the repeal of the house and window tax, the malt and hop duties – that each Englishman's house might have once again what it had in his (Mr. Penn's) young days – a barrel of beer in the corner. (Cheers and laughter) The present system of tythes was disgraceful, unjust and injurious to true religion. No man should be compelled to pay a commission to a minister with whom he could not have communion. What would the meeting think of forcing a person to pay a toll for Highgate-Archway if he had never been through it? (Loud laughter) That was the question that came home to all. It pressed not on the landlord alone, nor on the farmer, but the poor consumer. The poor paid 2s additional on every bushel of wheat for the tythe tax. (Cheers)

The returning officer put the candidates to vote. The show of hands for Mr. Barnard and Capt. Dundas was large. The show for the other candidates was less decided. The Returning Officer decided for Mr. Barnard and Capt. Dundas. A poll was demanded for Mr. Angerstein and Mr. Hammond and the date fixed. Mr. Penn came forward and resigned. The meeting closed.

All the points made by John Penn I and his manner of making them are almost pure Cobbett so it is clear that John Penn I must have read Cobbett's *Political Register* and other writings, but the possibility of a friendship is questionable. Cobbett had a friend called John Penn who provided financial support to him in 1800 and who was a descendant of William Penn of Pennsylvania and had a brother, Granville, in government service.[11] John Penn I was just starting his business in 1800, which makes it an unlikely time for him to have provided financial help. The demand for vote by ballot which Penn raised was one of the demands the reformers had dropped for tactical reasons. It seems that John Penn I's enthusiasm may have been greater than his political acumen. He probably realised that he would not succeed and put his name forward so that he could make a public statement of his views. His strong objection to the tythes, taxes to support the established church, may show that he was not a member of it. This could explain the lack of records of birth and marriage. His objections to pensions and sinecures arose from these being the consequence of patronage and favouritism.

The immediate reaction to the Act was that in social terms it did not go far to satisfy the growing hopes and expectations of most people. The Tolpuddle martyr incident in 1834 showed how the outdated repressive legislation could still be used. The working people organised themselves more and more and in 1838 brought forward the People's Charter which pressed for reform to go much further. The National Convention made a great display at Westminster but the Charter was rejected by parliament and subsequent rioting was handled effectively. However, Chartism remained a political force.

In 1835 the Admiralty decided to open up the supply of marine engines to more marine engineers and John Penn & Son and others were added to their list of approved suppliers.[12] Also in this year, a still seemingly unrelated event was that William Hartree completed his apprenticeship with John Courthope the stationer and was proposed by him to become a Freeman of the Honourable Company of Merchant Taylors. Soon after, on payment of £75:0:0, he became a Liveryman of the Company. Thomas Penn completed his apprenticeship with the firm in 1838.

The story of the *Beaver*, a paddle steamer built in 1835, with a Boulton & Watt engine operating at 5 psi, for Hudson's Bay Company service on the west coast of North America gives a little illustration of the fuel problems faced by a steamer.[13] She sailed, taking seven months, from the Thames to Port Vancouver at the mouth of the Columbia River with her paddle wheels as deck cargo. In coastal service she carried a crew of thirteen woodcutters and four stokers to keep her boilers supplied with fuel. The fuel on board left little space for trade goods and she was found to be of little use to the HBC. She was hired out to the Admiralty for survey work and, in 1888, ended life as a tug. That she kept going for over fifty years far away from well-equipped repair shops shows the potential life of these simple, robust engines.

In the 1830s and 40s a few naval officers who had become interested and enthusiastic about the possibilities of steam wrote books to educate and persuade their colleagues of its importance to the future of the Navy in terms of both technology and tactics. These books were genteelly written for easy reading by their unenthusiastic comrades. Naval traditions were all about seamanship and sailing.[14] There was little sympathy for this new, unnatural source of power, especially as it was dirty, unreliable and dangerous. The authors showed that they were prepared to overcome the common prejudices and to get their hands dirty; some even spent time in the workshops of marine engineers. Dirt related to steam was not just oil and grease in the engine room. One of the most unpopular tasks was taking on board the coal. All hands had to be put to work. The ship became filthy and several days of cleaning were required to return it the proper condition. There was also understandable concern about exploding boilers and the possibility of fire at sea as serious sources of danger. Further, the paddle wheels were totally exposed to enemy fire and the boilers and machinery could not be screened from incoming cannonballs. One consequence of these concerns was the Navy's preference for low steam pressures, which, in turn, led to undesirable higher coal consumption.

The first publication of the *Proceedings of the Institution of Civil Engineers* was in 1837. From then on the engineers had their own learned journal through which to share knowledge.

In 1837–9 John Penn & Son provided oscillating engines for seven Thames river steamers operating between Richmond and Westminster for the London, Westminster and Vauxhall Steam Packet Company.[15] The idea of the oscillating engine, in which the piston rods are connected directly to the crankshaft and the cylinders rock on trunnions through which the steam entered and left the cylinders, was not new. It avoided the use of a crosshead, working on precisely aligned guides, and a connecting rod between the piston rod and the crank, as seen on railway engines (see note at end of Chapter, p31). It proved very difficult to build reliable engines to this design although the concept was very attractive. Henry Maudslay and others built some but did not persist with the idea. John Penn II was determined to achieve a successful design. He altered some aspects of the previous designs to achieve a more ef-

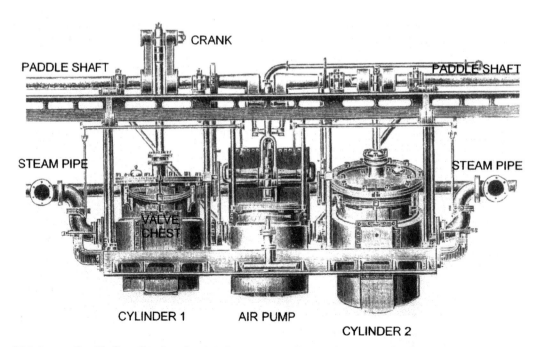

202 Penn Oscillating Engine for Waterman paddle steamers

ficient, compact and lighter engine. The most important changes were to take the valves away from the trunnions and to mount conventional valve chests on the sides of the cylinders, and to lighten the support frame. He then applied all his skill and that of his workmen to the accuracy of manufacture. This was the firm's first substantial order for oscillating engines. They became the first of a long line of very successful engines which, as his design innovations were copied by his competitors, effectively became the market leader design for paddle steamers for many years. This development is a good illustration of John Penn II's approach to innovation: be first to identify the needs of the customer and then create a design to meet them which was based on known technology and practice. It is a low-risk approach to technical progress and makes good sense to businessmen.

In 1838 an important opportunity arose for the firm which resulted in a close relationship being established between John Penn II and Thomas Ditchburn, who by then had built the fastest steamboat on the Thames. Ditchburn realised that the future was going to be with iron ships and that his employers were not going to make the change from wood. He went into partnership with Charles Mare to build the ships. They approached John Penn & Son about the supply of engines and the firm agreed to provide the machinery, oscillating engines of course, on credit.[16] This arrangement shows that the firm had a strong financial position at the time. An unexpected risk came from a fire, probably due to arson by wooden shipbuilder competitors, at Ditchburn and Mare's Deptford yard. They moved to the north bank in Canning Town and continued in business building ships of iron, wood or the two combined. That year John Penn & Son made its first sale to a foreign navy with the supply of engines for the Russian paddle steamer *Inkermann*; she was the first of twelve Russian navy vessels to be fitted with Penn engines.

A remarkable reminder of the firm at this time is the oscillating engine in the paddle steamer PD *Diesbar* of the Sächsische Dampfschiffahrt GmbH in Dresden. She was built in 1884 but her engine is a Penn oscillating engine of 1841, previously in the *Bohemia* [203, p28]. Many parts are not original but it is unmistakably a Penn oscillating design; compare Plate IVa with 202. With this engine PD *Diesbar* [204, p28] is still in operation as an excursion ship on the Elbe at Dresden (Appendix 2, p121).[17] There are similar examples of the installation of oscillating engines of the early 1840s in new British vessels in 1867 and 1871. Between 1840 and 1870 ten Elbe steamers were fitted with Penn engines which, in several cases, were subsequently installed in other new vessels. These simple engines had long lives.

Another very important development in marine engineering first came into view as a serious proposal in the late 1830s. This was the use of a screw propeller to generate the force to push the ship through the water. Through the 1840s and 50s it took on great importance for John Penn and Son: that story is told in Chapter 3. Many inventors had tried many ideas both in Britain and the USA, mostly concentrating on the shape of the propeller itself. It was in 1836 that Francis Petit Smith, a farmer who did all his work with models on a pond, took out the British patent which included the claim that the propeller was to be forward of the rudder so as to pick up the slow water in the wake of the hull and send a fast-moving stream of water towards the rudder which gave better steering capability. With his patent and model demonstrations he persuaded Lord Sligo to build a small boat which had successful trials on the Thames in 1837. The Ship Propeller Company was founded and the 200-ton *Archimedes* was built in 1838 at Limehouse with engines by Rennie. The name was chosen because the first propeller used was a true Archimedes screw. She made a demonstration journey to various ports and reached Bristol in 1840, where she was seen by I. K. Brunel and, following a trip to Liverpool, the decision was made to a use a propeller rather than paddles on Brunel's *Great Britain*.

204 *Diesbar*, Dresden 2005

203 *Bohemia*, 1841

In 1839 William Hartree, aged 25, married John Penn II's sister Charlotte Penn, aged 30. It is most likely that he was already in apprenticeship with the firm and that she had been housekeeping for her father after the death of her mother. Their first child, and John Penn I's first grandchild, a boy called William, was born in 1840. Sadly he died within a year. Another boy, also called William, was born in 1842 and a daughter, Louisa, in 1843. In 1845 they had another son, named John Penn after his grandfather. John Penn I had probably retired from the management of the firm by the time of young William's birth. He had interests in horticulture, with land to enjoy it, and astronomy, which he could share with his son-in-law. He could now add his grandson.

It was in the 1830s that John Hedges joined the firm.[18] He had served an apprenticeship as a millwright in Basingstoke and his father was friendly with John Penn I. In the course of his work he was involved in some experiments which involved the use of mercury and he left in 1841 suffering from mercury poisoning. It may be a coincidence but Thomas Howard of the King and Queen Ironworks in Rotherhithe, mentioned earlier, had an interest in a type of engine known as the Vapour Engine.[19] In this water was converted to steam very rapidly by spraying it onto a very hot surface so that it vaporised instantly. The iron vaporising surface was supported on a bed of mercury so that it could flex in response to variations of steam pressure and receive a good flow of heat from the firebox below. Howard also introduced the use of superheated steam and invented a special condenser, which, together with the engine, was intended to operate a closed, self-sufficient water cycle. Using this concept avoided the need for bulky boilers as the steam was made for each piston stroke as required. He approached the Admiralty and in 1835 HMS *Comet* was fitted with such a system, built by Maudslay; subsequently the system was fitted in two commercial vessels and HMS *Terrible*. They all operated for a few years and gave good savings in coal consumption but troubles with the failure of the vaporiser and the escape of hot mercury led to the concept being abandoned by the Navy. Further development of this may well have been the project Hedges was working on at Penn's. In 1840 John Matthew entered his apprenticeship with the firm.

By the end of the 1830s the Navy's attitude towards steam was changing. There had been a campaign at the east end of the Mediterranean where several armed steamers worked together with square-rigged ships of the line. In 1840 the commanding admiral expressed the view

> ...that the first battle would be in favour of the fleet with the greatest number of steamers.[20]

and another the view

> ...that steamers, if judiciously conducted, have the power to inflict merciless wounds with impunity so that a first-rate may be bled to death, without receiving a shot in return.[21]

He was referring to the paddle frigates, rigged with sails, which were armed fighting vessels and could use their superior manoeuvrability to harass the ships of the line. During the long sea voyages of the fleet they were towed by the sailing ships of the line. It became the Navy's policy to build a number of these paddle frigates which opened new opportunities for marine engineering in the 1840s. Also, in 1839, the Navy's first screw ship, *Dwarf*, constructed by Rennie, entered service.

In 1840 there was a 'Report of Commissioners on Steam Vessels Accidents' which led to a bill being proposed in parliament 'To Regulate Navigation by Steam'. A meeting of shipbuilders and engineers was held in London to consider the measures being proposed. The meeting, on considering

> ...the extensive powers proposed to be vested in the Commissioners and Inspector, came to the conclusion that such measures would be not only detrimental to their interests as a body, but highly prejudicial to the interests of the public by preventing fair and legitimate competition.

This was an early attempt at regulation being proposed during the heyday of laissez-faire economics and little government interference. The proposals came as quite a shock, although they do not look exceptional today. A committee was established to carry out the detailed examination of the proposed Act. John Penn II was a member, along with Thomas Ditchburn and other prominent figures in the industry.[22] This is the earliest record of his being asked to act in the interests of the profession and the industry; as a member of the engineering establishment.

The census of 1841 provides the first recorded information about the domestic situation of the Penn family. John Penn I was living in Lewisham Village at Riverdale House, which had a few acres of ground with a mill on the Ravensbourne, and other buildings. With him was his wife Rebecca, aged 28, clearly a second wife, and six house servants. The tythe records of 1843 show that he also occupied some neighbouring acres of garden and pasture. The entrance to the grounds was from Lewisham High Street opposite number 169. It is impossible to envisage today although the mill, with a CitiBank sign, can be seen opposite the Lewisham Centre [001, Area Map, p8] and Appendix 5, p124.

John Penn II, aged 30, was living in Coldbath Row with one female servant. William and Charlotte Hartree were living next door with one female servant. William Penn, brother of John Penn I, and his wife also lived in Coldbath Row. Coldbath Row was the name given to the row of houses on the south side of Blackheath Road which backed on to the Works site [412, Works Layout, p68].

In 1842 the firm had a contract to provide engines for twelve Thames paddle steamers of the Waterman Company. These, like the earlier order for seven, used oscillating engines with steam supplied by fire-tube boilers. This order consolidated the strong position of Penn's oscillating engine design for river steamers. John Hedges returned to the firm in 1843.

John Penn I died at his home in Lewisham on 6 June 1843. He had been ill for a long time. The surgeon had warned his wife that he would probably die suddenly. His brother William was at the house at the time of his death.[23] His will predates the probate procedures and was not valued. His son, John Penn II, was appointed executor and residuary beneficiary. His wife, Rebecca, was granted an annuity of £140 a year plus £100, his shares in the Ipswich, Warwick, Portsea Island and Poplar Gas Works, the grand piano and plate, £60 worth of furniture and the use of the house for six months. His brother William was granted £10,000. Thomas and William Howard, of the King and Queen Ironworks, Rotherhithe, were also granted £10,000 or £5,000 plus 5 per cent on £5,000 for ten years, but 'if they refuse or become incapable to consent or go to reside beyond the four seas then it shall be lawful for

205 Riverdale House, Lewisham

my daughter Charlotte Hartree to take the place'. The money was to be held in trust 'for the maintenance education and advancement of her children and grandchildren'. The place of the Howard brothers in the scheme of things is difficult to understand. Their inclusion in the will shows that they were well-trusted friends and it might have been that John Penn I had an understanding with them about the use of the money. Later in the will it is made clear that John Penn II was to become the residuary beneficiary on condition that the actions applying to Rebecca and William Penn were carried out and that a sum of £10,000 was to go to the trustees of his daughter Charlotte, with no mention of the Howard brothers. Charlotte's children and grandchildren did benefit from an inheritance on the terms of this will; £10,000 was a large sum of money in 1843 (see Chapter 4 p61). As residuary beneficiary John Penn II inherited the business and the properties.

It is clear that John Penn I had been very successful. Subsequent actions in the firm show that it was financially strong. The death of his first wife Charlotte is not recorded. It is not known when he married Rebecca but just prior to his daughter Charlotte's marriage would seem likely. Rebecca would have been about 30 at the time of his death and have cared for him in his last years. The annuity would continue if she remarried, the gas company shares would have added to it quite nicely; she had cared for him in old age and he provided for her in a sensible manner.

John Penn I had established the firm and, by his own skill and by the selection and training of the employees, had ensured it had a reputation for high-quality mechanical engineering work in several fields. He was fortunate to be able to see his son, whom he had trained, showing great skill and motivation and driving the business forward into marine engineering. The Institution of Civil Engineers included a note about him in the *Annual Report* for 1843.

Note on marine engines

The force required to propel a ship through the water increases with the weight of the ship as a ship displaces her own weight of water and that has to be moved as the ship proceeds. Engines, boilers and coal were all heavy items in the vessels of the times, which were mainly built of wood like sailing ships. It became important to create lighter and more efficient designs of engine to reduce weight and therefore reduce coal consumption – which again reduced weight. Beam and side-lever engines were heavy and bulky and many other designs were attempted.

A basic design problem was the connection of the piston rod, which moved in a straight line, to the crank, which rotated. Most designs achieved this by means of a guided crosshead at the free end of the piston rod on which was pivoted a connecting rod to the crank [206, p32]. For locomotives these designs were being made with inclined and horizontal cylinders; the concerns with piston and cylinder wear had diminished. Another solution was the oscillating engine which, although it was not his invention, John Penn II made his speciality. By mounting the cylinder, and hence the piston rod moving in it, on pivots or trunnions it was possible to connect the piston rod directly to the crank and avoid the need for the crosshead, slides and connecting rod. The cylinders rocked, or oscillated, to and fro as the crank rotated. The steam inlet and outlet, and the valves, were next to the central trunnion, caused the two cylinders to be widely separated [207, p32]. Penn's big development was to take the valves away from the trunnion, mount the valve chests on the sides of the cylinders and bring the cylinders closer together and so fit a larger, more powerful engine in the same space. The illustration, which is based on the *Diesbar* engine, shows some of the detail. This may seem a simple idea but a great deal of care and attention were required to make the resulting design into a reliable machine. He used wrought-iron rods in place of the conventional cast iron to lighten the frame. His design was copied by other marine engineers – Maudslay and Miller & Ravenhill – and became the standard oscillating engine design, as can be seen in the Science Museum display of models. Other engine builders had other solutions for the connection of the piston rod to the crank. Most of these engine types had special names: Siamese, Gorgon and Indirect, for example. Penn's oscillating engine and other types are well described in J. Bourne's *Treatise on Steam*, 5th edition, p305 *et seq.*

Penn also installed fire-tube boilers, which were more compact than cylindrical as their tubes gave a larger heating surface. The tubes were like ducts for the hot gases from the fire to pass through on their way to the funnel; hence the name fire-tube boilers. Boilers were constructed from riveted plates of wrought iron or copper. The tubes could be of cast iron. The fire-tube boiler held less water, saving weight again. Possible steam pressures increased as boiler and engine design improved. Increased pressure raises the boiling temperature. This makes the higher-pressure system intrinsically more dangerous. It is no wonder that very cautious attitudes were taken about pressure. Marine engines operated at lower pressures (10 to 20 psi) than locomotives and stationary engines (25 to 35psi) because of the more serious consequences of an explosion in a ship afloat.

The boilers designed by Perkins and Howard were attempts to use direct vaporisation of water on a hot surface rather than submerged boiling. Perkins tried to achieve this by a special arrangement of tubes and connecting passageways. Howard achieved it by having a large heating surface and spraying water onto it in just the amounts required for each stroke of the piston. Perkins's use of high pressures made sense with his steam gun but not for a marine engine. Howard used normal pressures and had some success. These were early precursors of the flash-tube boiler concept used today.

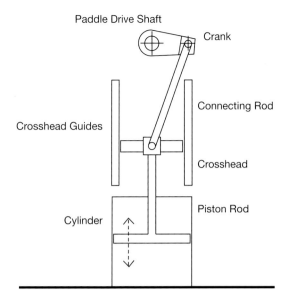

206 Engine with guided crosshead, diagram

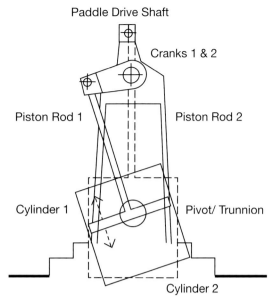

207 Oscillating Engine, diagram

208 *Diesbar* engine, showing valve chest

Steam in the boiler is at the temperature of vaporisation and will condense (return to water) when cooled. When steam entered the engine the cylinder was cool as it had just been connected to the cool condenser. Some condensation in the cylinder always occurred until the new warm steam heated it. This was a waste of heat. Two approaches were used to overcome this. One was to build an insulating jacket around the cylinder. The other was to superheat the steam; that was to heat it to well above the condensation temperature and eliminate the condensation of steam on entering the cylinder. The steam was superheated by passing through a heater using the hot flue gases from the firebox.

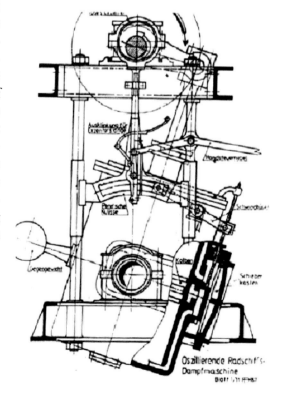

3. Success with Steam (1843–1856)

Steam marine engineering was now making significant advances and becoming more widely established. An 1840 comparison of transatlantic crossing times showed the steamer to halve the westward time and reduce the eastward to two thirds of that of a sailing ship. In 1842–3 *Driver* was the first steamer to circumnavigate the globe, largely under sail, but in 1846–9 *Inflexible* steamed 64,477 and sailed 4,392 miles in her circumnavigation. In 1845–6 paddle frigates were successful in action on the Parana River in Argentina.

In 1843 the Admiralty wished to increase the speed of the official yacht *Black Eagle* and needed more powerful engines to do this.[1] Boulton and Watt, who had built the original side-lever engines, were asked to quote for new ones. They replied that the engines required to give the vessel the desired speed would be too heavy for the ship and suggested that it would be better to build a new ship. The Admiralty were not prepared to go to that expense. John Penn II heard about this and, uninvited, sent the Admiralty a tender for the supply of an oscillating engine which would have twice the power of the existing Boulton & Watt engines, would be the same weight and take up less space. If the Admiralty were not satisfied with his engine he would remove it and refit the old ones. This was a very bold claim and it caught the interest of the Admiralty, even though it would be a much larger engine than any Penn had built so far. Also, despite the fact that many oscillating engines were in service there was prejudice against them; many people felt that the heavy engines rocking to and fro would destabilise the ship. When the Comptroller of the Navy was considering Penn's tender Sir John Rennie happened to call, so the Comptroller showed it to him and asked for his opinion. Rennie had experience with marine engines in general and knew something of oscillating engines. He said he thought the Navy should accept Penn's tender and agreed to take the blame if things turned out badly; this was a fine endorsement of Penn by a person held in high regard.

The engines were made, fitted on board the *Black Eagle* in 1844 and all the Admiralty requirements met. These were the first of the firm's oscillating engines to be installed on a sea-going, rather than a river or coastal vessel. From then on John Penn & Son became a major supplier of engines to the Navy. John Penn II's unsolicited bid and the firm's technical excellence had enabled them to break the naval supply dominance of Boulton & Watt and Maudslay, Son & Field. He must have had complete confidence in what he offered to do and known that he had the financial strength to survive if things went wrong. With the Navy's policy regarding the building of paddle frigates underway and its increased reliance on private shipbuilders rather than the naval dockyards the timing of this move by John Penn II was most fortunate. From 1846 he was supplying oscillating engines for naval sloops and mail packets. The most famous of the packets was the *Banshee*, which became the fastest in service. In 1850 Penn was asked to replace the Maudslay engines in the frigate *Retribution*.[2]

In the mid-1840s the firm took over the Deptford site on the riverbank [001, Area Map, p8]. It was immediately downstream from the Deptford Royal Dockyard, across Watergate Street at Payne's Wharf. Here they established their boilermaking facilities. The separation of boilermaking from engine building made good sense because the raw materials, the machines and the processes are quite different. Thomas Penn went there as engineer and later became foreman.[3] The addition of the Deptford site enabled the firm to expand the engine works in Greenwich and gave them waterfront access where they could either fit engines and boilers directly into ships or load them for transport to the yard where the ship was being fitted out. Raw materials could also be received from river traffic. It was an expedient way to expand but did not help overcome the poor location and layout of the Greenwich site. Watergate Street still runs down to the river and the boiler works site can be seen, best at low tide. The quite imposing arched riverfront remains and is listed, but there is not much more. The site is the subject of a development application which is under review at the time of writing. A curious small reminder of John Penn & Son's occupation of the site is a cast-iron bollard at the corner of Watergate and Borthwick Streets which bears their name; it is also listed. In 1844 John Matthew of the firm's design staff married William Hartree's sister Maria.

The first screw-driven ship for the Navy was *Dwarf*, constructed by Rennie in 1839. She was followed by *Rattler*, engine by Maudslay, in 1843. Performance data collected from her and *Dwarf* showed the advantages of the screw, over paddles, to convert power into ship speed, but a simple competitive trial was needed to convince the doubters. In this *Rattler*, with a so-called Siamese engine and gearing to the propeller shaft, towed her paddle-wheel sister ship *Alecto* backwards. This result put additional pressure on the doubters in the Navy, most of whom were likely not to be very keen on steam in any form. For the Navy propeller propulsion had several advantages over paddles. With the paddle wheels gone the side of the ship was clear for the full broadside of guns of a ship of the line; the ship could go alongside an enemy vessel and send a boarding party over; the fragile paddle wheels were no longer exposed to enemy fire and the engines and boilers could be placed low in the ship out of the enemy's line of fire.

Many technical and engineering problems remained to be solved to achieve efficient, reliable propeller drive systems for naval use. The major one was to develop engine designs that were sufficiently compact that they could be mounted low in the hull and that could run sufficiently

fast to give the rotational speed needed by the propeller without the use of gears. For commercial vessels the engines could be less compact as there was no danger from enemy fire and the familiar vertical or inclined cylinder designs and geared drives were favoured. Other problems needed combined shipbuilding and engineering solutions. Wooden ships flex as they ride the waves and this made it difficult to mount the long propeller shaft from the engine which, because of its weight, was near the centre of the ship, to the stern. Also the thrust from the propeller had to be carried on a special bearing which itself had to be supported on a very strong part of the hull.

John Penn II's approach to the problems of naval screw-propulsion was first to develop an engine design suitable for the direct drive of

301 Deptford bollard

the propeller shaft. His success with the oscillating engine as a more compact engine for paddle drive encouraged him. He again developed a design which dispensed with the connecting rod and guided crosshead and fitted the piston rod directly to the crank. He realised that higher rotational speeds were needed for propeller than for paddle and he chose to base his development on the trunk engine concept, an existing idea which he refined. A patent application was made covering the key features of the firm's trunk engine design. In 1845 it was granted in the names of John Penn, William Hartree and John Matthew.[4] He would have remembered how his oscillating engine design had been widely copied and wanted to avoid that with this new design.

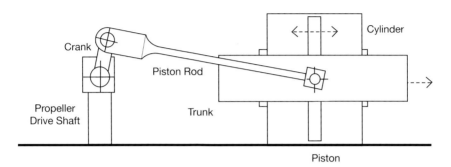

302 Trunk Engine, diagram

Here again John Penn II took proven design concepts and carefully modified them using known technology to achieve the performance which he knew was essential for success. It would be a low-risk innovation for the purchaser. Penn's trunk engines became the firm's next successful product after the oscillating engine and were not copied. They were designed to meet the needs of the Navy's fighting ships and were rarely used in merchant vessels; the P&O *Himalaya* of 1853 was one of the few [303, p36].

Almost every marine engine builder had his own preferred engine designs. Their relative merits are still debated amongst enthusiasts, although without experience of any of them. Penn's trunk engine is not favoured because of the perceived difficulties of maintaining the large seals where the trunk passes through the cylinder ends and of lubricating the connecting rod bearing, which is difficult to access inside the trunk. John Bourne does not mention these points in his *Treatise on Steam*[5] but we do know that very few trunk engines were installed in merchant ships. It is worth bearing in mind a brief comment by Robert Stephenson on marine steam engine patents, which comes from an 1855 letter regarding an engine patent.

> It is difficult to get other Engine Builders to adopt even a good plan when it is not their own. Look at Penn's patent Engine, no one pays him patent rights for his many excellent engines, the fact is that every form of Engine for Steam boats is merely a matter of compactness so the arrangements may vary in fifty different ways but still the performance of the Engines remains much the same.[6]

The selection of propeller design was difficult. There were a great number of patents for propeller designs by many inventors. The descriptions were not so specific as to make it clear just what was

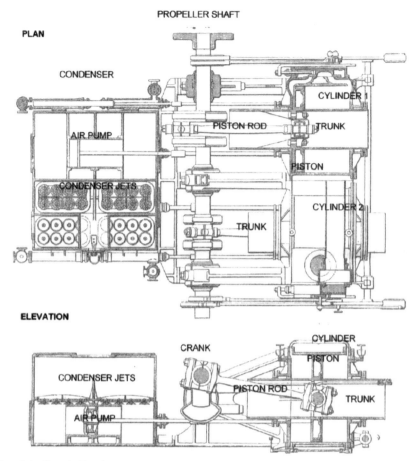

303 Penn Double Trunk Engine

being claimed or to separate the one from the other, so no one who used a design was sure to be free of a claim by a patentee. The Navy took a robust attitude towards the issue and made an offer to buy the rights to naval use of them all for the sum of £20,000, leaving it to the patent holders to decide how to share the money. The proposal was accepted and payment was made in two equal instalments in 1851 and 1855. Because of the weakness of the patents little money was made from commercial use, so this Admiralty settlement was about all the inventors received.

John Penn II's first appearance in court in a patent case came in 1844. A plaintiff named Lowe claimed that Penn had used a propeller design patented by a John Hunt. The court found for Lowe and Penn was instructed to pay 40s (£2.00) damages. Penn asked for a retrial. It took place in 1849 and found in favour of Penn.[7] The decision to have a retrial can hardly have been on commercial grounds about damages of two pounds. Penn must have believed there was a principle at stake. The case illustrates the difficulties raised by all the propeller design patents.

In the year of the trunk engine patent John Penn II became a full member of the Institute of Civil Engineers. Also in that year the firm was commissioned to install auxiliary screw propulsion engines using the patented design in existing ships of the line. The first were the sloops HMS *Phoenix* and *Encounter* launched in 1846.[8] That year the firm also supplied their first engine to the Spanish navy; they were followed by a further fifty-five.

At this time John Penn II had an opportunity for a project with William Ditchburn, who had been consulted by the Admiralty about the best way to convey Queen Victoria from Whitehall to Woolwich and had recommended the use of a screw-driven ship.[9] This was an almost too radical suggestion. One official suggested that 'Mr. Ditchburn's proposal to screw Her Majesty from Whitehall to Woolwich was very like high treason.' For the engines Ditchburn went to Penn and he used his oscillating type with gear drive to the propeller shaft. The *Fairy* was a great success and achieved thirteen knots – 'the fastest of any vessel propelled by screw' – and, as a Royal Yacht tender, was much appreciated by the Queen. *Fairy* was fitted out for sea-going service when the Queen went to Germany and Holland. For many years she accompanied the Royal Yacht on the Queen's tours around the British coast and was used to access smaller rivers and harbours. *Fairy*'s achievements and the publicity were very good for both Ditchburn's and Penn's reputations. Less than three years later a problem arose with one of the boilers on the *Fairy*.[10] It was not a major problem; the Admiralty were inclined to overlook it and did not act quickly. Prince Albert felt it was unreasonable for a boiler to require repair so soon in its life and commanded that it should be replaced. Penn agreed and the work was done. An officer who served on *Fairy* later said she 'was the most perfect gem that ever floated on the water'.

The year 1845 saw the Navy make the first significant change in the status of senior engineering officers, giving them warrant officer rank. Two years later they were given commissioned rank, but still as civil, not military, officers. Now they could use the wardroom, which was a significant social improvement in their situation, but they remained outside the command structure. There was pompous protest in the letter columns of the press condemning the change. Society was moving slowly but the Navy and the retired Admirals hardly at all. The first screw, not paddle, frigate was launched in 1846. For the remainder of the decade both screw and paddle frigates were built, the last paddle frigate being built in 1851. In 1845, although quite some years before the unification of Italy, the firm had its first Italian naval order.[11] Over the next forty years twenty-six Italian navy vessels were engined by the firm.

In 1847 John Penn II had reached the age of 42 and in that year he married. It is noticeable that both his father and sister had married quite late, he at 35 and she at 38, but 42 is even later. Could this have been a consequence of his rumoured French liaison, waiting for it to resolve in some way? This is pure speculation but it would be consistent with his honourable character. His bride was Ellen English, age 22, daughter of William English, an engineer from Enfield. Their first home was in Lewisham at Riverdale House. The first child was born in 1848, a boy named John – John Penn III. In that year John Penn II became a full member of the Institute of Mechanical Engineers. Their second child was born in 1849, a boy called William. In 1851 the third child, a son Frank, was born, and in 1853 a daughter, Ellen.

Overseas orders were not only for naval vessels. In the mid-1840s the firm had an order for four steam tug boats from the Mannheimer Dampfschleppschiffarhtgesellschaft (Steam Tug Boat Company).[12] The boats were built by Ditchburn and the engines by Penn. John Hedges, with his wife and twelve-year-old daughter, went to Mannheim as the Garantieingenieur (guarantee engineer) for the engines. After the four tugs had been delivered in 1848 he was asked to return to Penn's but did not as he had been offered a good job by the Mannheim Company. He was one of many British engineers who went abroad for their employers and stayed.

In the later 1840s, as the use of screw propulsion was increasing, the associated engineering problems other than the engine itself were becoming more apparent. An interesting example of the problems raised by the new technology was the problem of the drag of the stationary screw when proceeding under sail. John Penn & Son and others devised lifting frames and gear to raise the screw out of the water. These were large structures fitted at the stern of the ship. The screw could weigh many tons. The raising and lowering operations were tricky and required a large number of men on the ropes. On ships of that time manpower was the only power available to do anything other than propel the ship. Raising and lowering the anchor, raising the sails, pumping the bilges were all done by manpower, using many men. The combined operation of raising and lowering the screw and lowering and raising the telescopic funnel was the origin of the order 'Up Funnel, Down Screw' for the change from sail to steam.

The 1840s had been good for business and it seems likely that the continued political pressures from the Chartists and the Anti Corn Law Leaguers were of small concern to a man so occupied with his business as John Penn II. The fact that the political venture is not mentioned in any of the accounts of his father's life and that he never sought office himself makes it likely that he did not have strong political interests.

By the end of the decade the firm would have been employing at least five hundred people. John Penn was well respected by them. His own skills enabled him to demonstrate how their work could be improved and he achieved a family-like relationship with them. No doubt they were, to him, 'his men'. It was said that John Penn II

> ...would trust no underhand information. He trusted himself – his eyes, his own hands, his own facilities. His great undertaking centred on himself.[13]

A rumour has it that Edward Humphrys, a very fine engineer, worked at Penn's for some time. A difference arose between him and John Penn II which led to Humphrys leaving, maybe being asked or told to go. This is not surprising; Humphrys went on to become an engineering entrepreneur himself and strong-minded entrepreneurial people often disagree. However, John Penn II was one of those who supported Humphrey's application for membership of the Institution of Civil Engineers in 1848.[14] That year William Hartree joined the Institution of Mechanical Engineers and became a partner in the firm. In 1849 John Matthew, now chief designer and a partner of the firm, had become a member of the Institute of Civil Engineers, proposed by John Penn II.

Britain's social and political disturbances in the late 1840s were very mild in comparison with those in the statelets of Germany and in France. The 1848 revolutionaries at the barricades in Germany were quickly crushed and most imprisoned. In France the popular movement brought an end to the reign of Louis Philippe and replaced it with a republic. Louis Napoleon, who as a nephew of Bonaparte had always seen himself as the successor to the Emperor's throne, was elected President in 1850 and by 1852 had become Emperor as Napoleon III. He had spent two periods of exile from France in England. He wished to overcome the historical enmity between France and England and realised that France could not achieve greatness again without Britain as an ally.

The British Admiralty had always considered France as the number one enemy and its warship design policies were under review. The main issue was between sail-only and sail with steam auxiliary; the second was between paddle and screw for the auxiliary drive. In 1850 a squadron of sail-only and steam auxiliary paddle and screw frigates took part in what became known as the Lisbon Trials.[15] Their performance was tested in ways which were relevant to battle conditions, unlike the earlier simple *Rattler* and *Alecto* demonstration. HMS *Arrogant*, with Penn trunk engines, showed very good sailing performance and excellent machinery reliability. Hers was an important contribution to the Admiralty's policy for an end to sail-only warships and the use of screw rather than paddle for the auxiliary drive. All would have screw auxiliary steam power to give extra manoeuvrability in calm and light winds and to give them a great advantage over purely sailing ships of the line.

It was realised that such vessels were easy targets for land-based forts because they had to present their full broadside silhouette to the fort if they were to bombard it. The French had strong harbour defences so the 'Cherbourg' strategy was devised. In this the bombardment of the fort would be the task of smaller steam-powered gunboats which could keep moving whilst bombarding and were much more difficult targets for the guns on the forts. This increased reliance on steam re-emphasised the need to overcome the social and organisational problems of the navy, but with no immediate effect.

In 1851 the Navy ordered its first ship of the line to be designed, rather than adapted, as a steam-screw auxiliary, HMS *Agamemnon* (Plate IIa).[16] The machinery was not fitted before launching so there is no propeller to be seen in the space between the stern and the rudder post. She was fitted with trunk engines by John Penn & Son. This was the first of three significant 'firsts' for the firm. Also that year a proposal came forward from some Irish investors for a packet service from Galway to Halifax, Nova Scotia. A sum of £50,000 was to be raised and it was agreed that Miller Ravenhill would build the vessels with John Penn & Son supplying the engines.[17] It is a bit reminiscent of the *Ipswich* and *Suffolk* project, but came to nothing.

This was also the year of the Great Exhibition in the Crystal Palace in Hyde Park. According to the catalogue John Penn & Son were there on the ground floor in N aisle exhibiting

> ...pair of marine oscillating engines, and pair of patent marine engines on the trunk principle, for the driving of screw propellers direct. Working models of marine oscillating engines, and of patent trunk engines and donkey engine.

A donkey was a small engine with its own boiler. On a ship it could be operated independently of the main engine and used to provide power for tasks such as bilge pumping or hoisting and lowering loads which had previously been done by manpower. There was a total of 1,000 exhibits in the section Machines for Direct Use. That year William Hartree became an Associate of the Institute of Civil Engineers, proposed by John Penn II; he succeeded to full membership in 1856.

It was also a census year, which gives another glimpse into domestic life. John and Ellen Penn were living with John III, aged 3, William, aged 1, and an 'unnamed son of three weeks' – Frank – plus seven servants at Riverdale House in Lewisham, the property he had inherited from his father. The Hartree family with five children, three house servants and a monthly nurse were still living in Coldbath Row. William is described as an Engineer and Manager at John Penn & Son employing 333 men and boys at the Greenwich Works. Thomas Penn was living in 10 and 11 Butcher's Row, Deptford, with his wife and daughter; he is described as Engineer and Foreman.

In 1852 the new owners of the *Great Britain* decided to fit new engines. Originally the largest iron-hulled vessel of her time, she had been fitted with an engine designed and built in Bristol which drove the propeller shaft through gears to achieve the required rotational speed. The job of providing the new engine was given to John Penn and Son, who fitted an oscillating engine which could operate in the same way as the original. The decision to use propeller drive on *Great Britain* had been taken back in 1840 but her maiden voyage had been delayed until 1845 because of financial difficulties. A year later she had gone aground on the Irish coast. She survived thanks to Brunel's hull construction but the company which owned her did not. She was sold for use on the Australian route. She went on to do service in the Crimean War. She is now restored and is open to the public at the dry dock in Bristol where she was built. The engine is a replica of the original but there are references to Penn in the museum display. That year John Penn II was in a delegation from the Association of Employers of Operative Engineers to make representation at the Home Office; Joshua Field and William Fairbairn were also there.[18]

In 1853 the Admiralty were considering designs for a new, faster paddle-driven Royal Yacht. Penn had put in a tender for large oscillating engines. There were still some in the Admiralty who were not entirely happy with the concept, especially with very large cylinders. Their unease reached the attention of Prince Albert, who requested a letter from the Admiralty explaining their decision to use Penn's engines. The letter shows how confused the thinking could be. The doubter was also concerned about the boiler pressure and wished to lower it. He seemed to have forgotten that a lower pressure would require even larger diameter cylinders than those to which he was already objecting.[19]

There was one more technical problem to be solved before screw propulsion could become a truly practical proposition. In paddle ships the paddle wheel drive shaft and the bearings in which it turned were across the beam of the ship above the waterline. The propeller drive shaft went along the length of the ship and came out at the stern below water, so the stern bearing was under the waterline. With the packing materials available at the time it proved impossible to stop water entering the stern bearing, washing away the lubricating grease, based on animal or vegetable fats, and leaving the wrought-iron shaft rotating without lubrication in the bronze or white metal bearing and wearing it away very quickly. Once the bearing had worn the shaft was free to rattle about and cause vibrations which shook the wooden hull apart. There are many stories of ships having to stop because too much water was coming in and even of the loss of the propeller itself through fatigue failure of the shaft. The wear of the bearing was worst when the ship was steaming in muddy, sandy and hence abrasive, shallow coastal waters, yet this was where auxiliary propeller drive could be most useful. This situation had to be overcome before propeller drive could be a practical proposition for long-distance cruising.

John Penn II was strongly aware of the problem and determined to find a solution. He employed Francis Petit Smith, who had fallen on hard times, to carry out experiments on a wide variety of materials for possible use in stern bearings. An experimental rig was built at the Greenwich Works which could be used to compare the performance of samples of possible bearing materials working underwater. A range of both metals and woods was tried. It was known that wood had been used in watermill bearings where load conditions were less severe. The woods all outperformed the metals by a large margin. The best was the tropical wood known as lignum vitae. The tests subjected the wood to loadings well beyond the design requirements of propeller shaft bearings so the results could be used with total confidence. Based on the results of these tests bearing designs were developed in which dovetailed strips of the wood were inserted into slots made along the length of the bronze bearing bushes. The wood strips stood proud from the bronze bushes and carried the load. There were gaps between them so that seawater could flow through the bearing and help keep it cool. There was a seal at the inboard end of the bearing but some water would always leak through, collect in the bilges and be pumped out. A lignum vitae bearing bush which worked for 200,000 miles in the SS *Royal Charter* can be seen at the Science Museum store (see Appendix 5).

305 Lignum Vitae propeller shaft stern baring

In 1854 John Penn II took out a patent to protect his invention.[20] He applied it as soon as he could convince his customers of its effectiveness. He licensed others to make the bearings at a royalty of 2/6d per horsepower (£125 per 1,000 ihp) on the shaft . Shaft horsepower could range from tens to thousands so the patent provided good earning opportunities. The experimental work showed that this was another virtually no-risk innovation. It is another excellent example of innovation based on good research and understanding of the subject. In 1856 and 1858 F. P. Smith and John Penn II presented papers to the Institute of Mechanical Engineers describing the tests and operating experience. The concept was taken up quickly and has been recognised as an essential element in the universal use of propeller-drive propulsion. Most authorities claim that the value of this invention to the growth in the use of steam power for ships cannot be overrated.

In the same year the France to Britain rapprochement led by Napoleon III was already having an effect and John Penn II joined with Joseph Whitworth, the world's most famous builder of machine tools, and the Surveyor and the Controller of the Navy to make a visit to France to exchange ideas and information about naval ships and marine engineering.[21] This appointment is another demonstration of the reputation John Penn II had achieved.

The year 1853 saw a changing emphasis in international relations. Britain developed an anti-Russian attitude. This was made up from several strands. One was the possibility of Russia's eastward expansion becoming a threat to the northern borders of India; it continued to the end of the century as the Great Game. Another was concern about Russia's intentions regarding the Ottoman Empire. Russia had a large navy but, with it based at Kronstadt close to St Petersburg, at Sevastopol on the Black Sea and at Murmansk, had no well-located all-season port with ocean access. Sevastopol was open all-season but without permission from the Ottoman Empire the fleet could not leave the Black Sea and get into the Mediterranean. Britain's concern was whether Russia had hidden intentions to gain land control of the Bosphorus and Dardanelles. There was also a public view that Russia was a despotic and barbaric country which should not be allowed to get 'too big for its boots'. Russia's every move was closely watched. France's concerns were more with the balance of power in Europe and the way in which Russia's actions could upset it. Napoleon III realised that France and Britain both had concerns regarding Russia and saw an opportunity to form an alliance for an action which would improve France's international standing to what he saw as its rightful place.

A petty-sounding dispute arose between Russia and the Ottoman (Turkish) Empire over the steward-ship of the Christian holy places in Jerusalem. Should the Orthodox or the Catholic churches have the responsibility? France saw herself as the champion of the Catholic cause and Russia saw itself as champion for the Orthodox. Britain did not have concerns over this issue but had to watch for the consequences. In early autumn 1853 Russia moved troops westward along the north coast of the Black Sea into Ottoman territory. The outcome was that Russia and Turkey went to war. Russia made no great advance before the campaign season ended. The Turks then sent a flotilla eastward along the south coast of the Black Sea to answer a Russian bombardment at Batoun at the east end of the Black Sea. The fleet stopped at Sinope and there was attacked and almost totally destroyed by the Russian fleet from Sevastopol. It was the first major use of exploding shells, as opposed to solid cannonballs, in a naval action. This caught the attention of the British who had trained the Turkish navy. After more diplomatic talking Britain and France formed an alliance and in March 1854 declared war on Russia. This was the start of what we know as the Crimean War; truly the Russian War of the allies Turkey, France, Britain and the Kingdom of Sardinia.

During the several months leading up to the war secret plans were being prepared. Britain had not been involved in a major land war since Waterloo. There was no standing army or War Department to supply one. The navy had reduced in size but had retained its historic role and support organisation. The Admiralty knew that it must be ready to put two strong fleets to sea. One would be needed in the Baltic to blockade the Russians behind Kronstadt at St Petersburg and one in the Black Sea to blockade Sevastopol and support the landing of troops. The fleets had to be able to take on strongly defended coastal positions. The conversion of the remaining sailing ships of the line to screw auxiliaries and the building of gunboats, as in the 'Cherbourg' strategy, were priorities. The Admiralty commenced secret discussions with the major private shipyards and marine engineers. John Penn II was consulted; he is the only one named in Sir J. H. Briggs's record.[22] Political prevarication and the need for secrecy meant no action could be taken until war was declared.

The firm continued with contracts for auxiliary steam screw conversions, one of which was the *Corn-wallis*, which became the only ship in the Baltic fleet to be hit by enemy fire.[23] It also made a major contribution to the supply of engines for the gunboats. After the 1854 campaign the Admiralty realised that more would be needed for 1855 when half the one hundred vessel Baltic fleet was to be gunboats and mortar vessels. For the proposed Kronstadt campaign of 1856 this number was more than doubled. The wooden hulls for these small vessels could be made in most shipyards and the work was contracted out by the naval dockyards. A total of 156 gunboats of five different Classes were built in 1854–56.

306 HM Gunboat *Magnet*, Albacore Class, 1856

For the supply of gunboat engines John Penn & Son and Maudslay, Son & Field were chosen as the two main contractors.[24] Penn was responsible for 97 engines in all classes and Maudslay for 59 in two classes. Each firm had its own designs of engine. For most of his engines Penn used a small trunk engine operating at a high pressure of 60 psi – large trunk engines were using 20 psi (Appendix 2, p120). Because of the firms' workload for larger engines subcontracting arrangements were made with other engineering firms for the gunboat engines. Penn and Maudslay would provide the patterns for castings and drawings showing the machining dimensions and no doubt had someone checking quality at the subcontractors. At that time there were no national standards of measurement and most workshops used their own length and screw thread standards. The Admiralty showed great technical awareness and required all the contracting workshops to work in accordance with the Whitworth measurement standards.[25] The benefit of this was that a 'not very large floating workshop was able to look after all the repairs for the Baltic Fleet'; a point emphasised by *The Times* which was supporting the idea of national standards. There was standardisation of each firm's engines but this would not have meant complete interchangeablility of parts even within engines of the same size and maker. The manufacture of all these engines in so short a time was a very impressive feat of manufacturing management. Although not really mass production, as is sometimes claimed, it illustrated the role the new engineering industry could play in national strategy. In the obituary of Whitworth on 24 January 1887 *The Times* gives a more graphic, factually incorrect and almost mythical version of John Penn's contribution to gunboat engine manufacture in 1884–5.

The steam navy was expensive. The Supplementary Navy Estimates for 1854–5 had £537,331 devoted to steam. That was in a total estimate of £11,000,000. In 1855–6 the Supplementary for steam was £1,797,366 and to this was added a Supplementary beyond the Ordinary and Supplementary of £550,000; that is a total of £2,347,366 Supplementary on top of an Estimate of £13,000,000. The Supplementary beyond the Ordinary and Supplementary led to stern letters from the Exchequer to which the Admiralty replied that they were taking money from some other part of their budget, just as happens today. The rising cost of the new defence technology was becoming apparent, and worrying.

From the ship and engine data referred to in Appendix 2 the total value of John Penn & Son's share of this can be estimated. The machinery for the gunboats supplied in 1854–6 was worth £220,000 and that for the twenty corvettes, frigates and ships of the line £370,000; a total of £590,000.

The naval war took a different course in each of the two seas. The allied Fleet entered the Baltic in March 1854, ensured there were no Russian vessels in the Baltic ports or at Bomarsund, the Russian base in the Alano Islands, and then threw a blockade across the Gulf of Finland. As the ice melted the fleet moved east and brought the blockade to Kronstadt without any resistance. The shallow draught steam frigates and gunboats were used to carry out accurate charting of the waters of the Alano Islands and of the waters along the Finnish coast to Kronstadt; Finland was a part of Russia then. The presence of this combined British and French fleet, which carried mainly French troops, within sight of St Petersburg was felt as a real threat to the capital. Russia held some 200,000 guards regiment troops back for its defence and so could not send them to serve in the Crimea. This major strategic achievement for the Allies required no significant battles, almost no losses and is largely forgotten. As a demonstration of naval power the Russian base at Bomarsund was attacked and taken. The charting work which had been done enabled the steam fleet to make

307 Steam auxiliary fleet approaching Bomarsund,
led by paddle frigate HMS Lightning

a surprise attack in which losses were small. The fleet withdrew in the autumn and was back on station the following spring. The blockade continued and the high point of the campaign became the bombardment of Sveaborg, the defensive fort of Helsinki. This was not important in itself but served to show the Russians what the fleet could do to Kronstadt, thus increasing the reality of the threat to the capital. Gunboats, steam batteries and mortar ships, all the small vessels with Penn and Maudslay engines, were the main source of the bombardment. Superior charting and the manoeuvrability of steam vessels were vital also; the Russian charts had shown the waters used by the bombarding fleet as shoals.

The strategic objective in the Black Sea was the capture of Sevastopol. The allied fleet quickly took command of the sea to secure the allies' supply lines, blockaded the Russian fleet in Sevastopol and cut the sea supply route from the mouth of the Dnieper to the Crimea. The landing of troops on the Crimean peninsula was supported with the bombardment of coastal defences and of Sevastopol itself, another important use of the gunboats. The Admiral in command of the Black Sea fleet was none other than Captain Dundas, against whom John Penn I had stood in the Greenwich election of 1832. It seems unlikely Dundas realised that many ships of his fleet had engines made by the son of one of his opponents of twenty years earlier.

The awfulness and appalling management of the land campaign on the Crimea is well known. But it is often forgotten in Britain that of the 224,000 allied troops there in 1855 only 32,000 were British. There were 120,000 French, 55,000 Turkish and 17,000 from the Kingdom of Sardinia. Casualties, mainly from disease, were high and the French losses were the highest. In 1854 and well into 1855 the campaign was at a stalemate. In 1855 an important naval operation using shallow-draught gunboats and others was to capture the entrance to the Sea of Azov, to take command of that sea and to disrupt entirely the supply of fodder and provisions from the Don River basin to the Crimea. This further weakened the Russians' ability to hold their positions and in September 1855 French troops stormed the Malakof redoubt which was the key to the defence of Sevastopol. The war's strategic objective had been achieved and the land campaign came to an end. In October there was a naval bombardment of Kinburn, the fort at the mouth of the Dnieper. Like the bombardment of Sveaborg, it was a demonstration to show the Russians the possible consequences of furthering the war. The gunboats were at it again.

During the winter of 1855–6 diplomacy took over from campaigning. Britain rather wanted to hit the Russians hard to show them who was on top and ordered the building of more gunboats for an attack on Kronstadt. The French had suffered much greater losses and felt their objectives had been achieved. Austria joined in the diplomacy and Russia agreed to a peace in March 1856. The April 1856 Fleet Review before Queen Victoria, consisting of two hundred and forty fighting ships – ships of the line, frigates, sloops, armoured batteries and gunboats – was a powerful demonstration of Britain's naval and industrial superiority.

In both the Baltic and the Black Sea fleets the younger, steam enthusiast officers had felt frustrated by the attitudes of their superiors who did not appreciate the possibilities of steam-engined ships. Sir J. H. Briggs also comments on the attitude of Dundas, who did not want to accept that war was really coming; even when the troopships had passed into the Black Sea he was still hoping for a negotiated settlement. Dundas had recently taken a new, young wife so he would have wished not to have to go into combat. Memorial tablets for Dundas and both his wives in can be seen in Kintbury church in Berkshire.[26]

The situation of engineer officers in the Navy remained unchanged. Recruitment was difficult. It is apparent that the ranking military officers still did not appreciate the responsibilities of the engineers. They would not, of course, have read John Bourne's 1853 third edition of *Treatise on Steam*. In the section entitled *Management* he devotes seven pages to the management of marine engines and only one to the management of land locomotives. This was because

> ...marine engines require more intelligence than any other description, partly because of their great size and complication and partly on account of the serious consequences accident may entail...the engineer is reliant on only his own resources for any breakage, repair etc. at sea or distant port...

The Navy were still treating the men with this intelligence, resource and skill as second-class members. It is no wonder that they felt aggrieved.

Many of the gunboats had been built of unseasoned timber and were not fit for a long working life. Several did continue in naval service for some years and many were sold to ship-breakers, the engines removed and installed in merchant ships. In 1983 a Penn gunboat engine was discovered in the wreck of the cargo ship *Xantho* (Plate IVb) [307] off the west coast of Australia. It is restored and on display at the Western Australia Maritime Museum's Shipwreck Museum in Fremantle.[27] It is the only original trunk engine in existence (see Appendix 5, p124). These little gunboats with their complement of no more than thirty-six officers and men must not be confused with the ships used for 'gunboat diplomacy'. A more substantial threat was needed for that: a ship with a larger complement of men so that an impressive landing could be made to subdue and overawe the natives.

307 Xantho engine,
view from above (left) and rear (right)

The war had not threatened the territorial integrity of Britain; it had been fought far away and, although it was the first war to be reported fast by telegraph, it was a remote event for most people. Domestic life was not much affected. Firms with military and naval contracts prospered. John Penn & Son was one of these and must have done well. In 1855–6 the three partners, John Penn II, William Hartree and John Matthew all made major personal investments in property and houses. John Penn II purchased an estate of fifty-five acres in Lee called Lee Grove, on the south side of Blackheath north of Belmont Hill. The house was extensively remodelled by the architect John Thomas with an Italianate exterior and the interior redecorated by J. G. Grace of Cavendish

308 The Cedars, North front

Square. The gardens were improved. Penn made an application to divert the narrow old road in front into a new wider road and to preserve the row of stately elm trees which bordered the old road. The old road became part of the property and a main entrance lodge with elegant iron gates was built. It was renamed The Cedars after the fine cedars of Lebanon in the grounds (Appendix 5, p124 and Area Map, p8). The result was 'a fitting abode for a merchant prince'.[28] The house can still be seen, a red sandstone building on the opposite side to St Margaret's church and a bit to the west. It has been converted into flats and is surrounded with new apartment blocks. Also in 1856 John Penn II made a post-nuptial settlement to his wife Ellen.

William and Charlotte Hartree's new property was Morden Hill House, off the Lewisham Road near Greenwich and the works (001, Area Map, p8). There is nothing to be seen now. The area suffered bomb damage in World War II and has been completely rebuilt. It was a substantial house to which he added a library and an observatory. The library was to house his collection of books, which was later the subject of an eight-day sale by Sotheby's, and the observatory was to house a five-inch refracting telescope by Thomas Cooke which had won a silver prize at the 1852 Paris Exhibition.[29] He was enjoying the best of things. In 1855 and 56 William Hartree and John Penn II applied for and were granted Arms by the College of Heralds. John Matthew bought Burford Lodge estate near Dorking with its house and also the Hare and Hounds inn, now Burford Bridge Hotel.[30] In the house he set up a reflecting telescope, installed a fine turret clock and had a small workshop for his recreational interest of instrument making. All three partners were showing great confidence in the future of their firm and their social standing.

The investments of the partners can also be seen as expression of their commitment to the Greenwich and Deptford locations of the business. This was very natural for them as they would have seen the firm as consisting of the skilled men they employed there. They were probably not aware of the view expressed by David Napier, the Clyde-based shipbuilder and marine engineer in 1852.

> London will never be a place for building steamers on account of everything connected with their production being higher than in the North.[31]

However, it is hard to believe that John Penn II did not know the views of his friend John Bourne, the great writer on all aspects of steam engineering business. He wrote, in relation to marine engine manufacturing,

> ...the best situation appears to be in a coal and iron district open to the sea and attending any means of transport, both railway and canal.

309 John Penn II, ca 1858

He goes on to say:

> ...large towns are not eligible situations for such engine works...the cost of subsistence is greater than in secluded districts, and the wages of operatives must be higher to purchase the same amount of comfort, or else his comfort may be diminished.[32]

He further writes that the best site will be rectangular with the factory laid out in large rectangular buildings. Strangely he does not mention that a level site is best for the handling of large heavy objects. Neither the location of the firm's main site in Greenwich, which had been chosen before marine engineering existed, nor its layout, came near to matching any of these best criteria. The partners were experiencing good profits, had a full order book, and if they read it, probably saw Bourne's comment as a writer's theorising and of no relevance to them.

In 1855 John Penn II undertook to rebuild the Symington engine from the Dalswinton Lake trials of 1788. It had been rescued from a scrap heap in Scotland. It is now exhibited in the Marine Engineering collection at the Science Museum.[33]

Note on trunk and gunboat engines

Penn's trunk engines used for driving the propeller shafts of ships of the line were installed with the cylinders horizontal and the piston rods directly driving a crankshaft which was in line with and connected to the propeller shaft. The engines were installed low in the hull, below the waterline. They operated at quite low pressure, about 20 psi.

Penn's trunk engines and other designs of engines for screw propeller ships are well described in John Bourne's *Treatise on Steam*, 5th edition, pp313–4 and p404.

Penn's gunboat engines were also of the trunk design. They were not condensing engines as the steam was exhausted to atmosphere directly from the cylinder. They used seawater as the source of steam and were designed to operate at a higher pressure of 60 psi. This meant that a smaller engine could be used to generate the required power. They were innovative for their time, were cheap to build and not expected to have a long service life (see Appendix 2, p120).

Note on lignum vitae stern bearings

These bearings were designed to work in water so they were installed with no seal at the outer end. At the inboard end there was a sealing gland of packing material which could be compressed onto the propeller shaft by tightening the bolts of the gland ring. When in harbour or cruising under sail with the shaft not turning the gland ring bolts would be tightened to stop the ingress of water. When the shaft was to turn the bolts would be loosened, at first to allow a trickle and then, as speed increased, to provide sufficient flow to avoid overheating, judged by the temperature of the water flowing through. The wood lignum vitae comes from the evergreen tree Guiacum officinale, native to the West Indies.

4. A VERY REPUTABLE FIRM (1856–1867)

The Russian (Crimean) War had been a very busy time for the firm. The gunboat orders were not completed until after the peace terms had been settled, with the largest number being built in 1856. Engines were also provided in 1856 for three ships of the line. The firm's reputation had been further enhanced by its wartime contribution. The war had shown up the inefficiencies of the government's organisation, especially in the War Department. The staffing of the civil service was not professional. There were many allegations of favouritism and patronage which led to committees of enquiry. These enquiries resulted in civil service recruitment based on examinations and merit, hence bringing an end to patronage. Sir J. H. Briggs, in his memoirs of Naval Administrations, refers to complaints about favouritism for John Penn & Son.[1] The firm had been granted contracts when they had not been the lowest bidders. He defended the Navy's position.

...engines supplied to the line-of-battleships by that firm were delivered punctually and found to work with such perfect success, that the only trials deemed necessary before proceeding on active service were those that took place in the short run between the Nore and the Downs merely to ascertain whether their bearings heated or not; whilst the *James Watt*, a line-of-battleship with a complement of six to seven hundred men, with engines supplied by another firm at a lower tender, was precluded from proceeding to her station for several months as a consequence of the defections and the unsatisfactory conditions of her machinery; and this at a time when her services were urgently required on active service.

In 1858 an Admiralty Committee was set up to make recommendations about the sourcing of marine engines for the fleet. The conclusions were:

...that, of all the variety of engines that have been purchased by the Government for our screw ships of war, the following are so far superior to all others that no engines of an older make should ever again be put on board. The engines to which they now refer to are:

1st. The single piston-rod engine, with the connecting rod attached direct to the crank shafts, and with a single flat guide.
2nd. The engine commonly known as the trunk engine, and patented by Messrs. John Penn.
3rd. The double piston rod engine. [This is the reverse connecting rod engine of Maudslay]

There can be no doubt, as already stated, that these three forms of construction for engines are not only better suited for the Navy than any other kinds that have been purchased for men-at-war, but also that they are better suited for those purposes than any modifications of the steam engine that have as yet been constructed.

...have arrived at the conclusion that for very small engines the single piston-rod engine, as adapted by Messrs Humphrys, Tennant & Dyke, is the engine best suited for the Navy.

...that up to 300 collective nominal horse-power there is no engine for men-of-war superior to the single piston-rod engine, with a single flat guide.... And that the trunk engine, as constructed by Penn & Son, has answered so extremely well, more particularly where great power is required, that the Committee recommend that, with such improvements in the details of these two engines as experience points out, they should be considered for the present naval engine.[2]

This was a recommendation indeed; it reads almost like a Penn monopoly for the large engines. The Humphrys of Humphrys, Tennant & Dyke is the engineer who worked briefly for Penn. Their works was in Deptford close to Penn's Boiler Works.

In 1857 the Penns' second daughter, Isabella, was born. Also John Penn II was asked to serve on a committee with Robert Stephenson, John Field and others to select the machinery for the Deptford pumping station which was important to the sewage removal scheme for the south shore of the Thames being carried out by Joseph William Bazalgette.[3] The two main sewers on the south bank joined to pass under Deptford creek. The sewage had to be lifted from the tunnel and pumped on its way to the Crossness outfall. Four beam engines and ten Cornish boilers were installed. The pumphouse is still in place but operates with electric motors.

In this year John Penn II was granted his patent for the use of wood in the bearings to carry the thrust of the propeller. It complemented the earlier patent for the wooden rotational bearings. This was also the year of the first order from the German navy; there were nine more orders over the next twenty years. In 1858 there was the first engine for the Brazilian navy with a further ten by 1879. Peru had four sets of engines between 1852 and 1874 and Japan three between 1853 and 1877.[4]

In 1858–9 John Penn II, having been a Vice-President for several years, was elected President of the Institution of Mechanical Engineers and was made a life member of the Institution. The Institution was then based in Birmingham and his attendance at meetings was not frequent. He presented the second paper on wood for the stern bearings of propeller shafts. In 1859 he received the very significant honour of becoming a Fellow of the Royal Society; cited as

> John Penn CE (Civil Engineer). The Inventor of Several Parts of Marine Steam Engines and Machinery Connected with Steam Navigation. Distinguished for his aquaintanceship with the science of mechanics. Eminent as a Mechanician and Engineer. From personal knowledge John Penn CE (Civil Engineer). Signed W Cubitt; Thos. Sopwith; Joseph Whitworth: Rob. Stephenson and others.[5]

There is no record of his taking an active part in the proceedings and, for him, it was most likely a place to meet fellow London-based engineers and also provided the opportunity to meet a wide variety of interesting people from different fields of activity. Many of these would have been invited to the summer evening gatherings he hosted at The Cedars,

> …where might be seen men of the highest distinction in art, science and literature – the best engineers, the best painters, the best philosophers.[6]

Both the firm of John Penn & Son and John Penn II himself had now achieved fine reputations in their business and profession.

During this time he kept his personal engineering interests and contacts alive. An archived letter of 24 March 1858 to Joshua Field about coal consumption in corn milling is clearly part of an ongoing conversation on the subject. It contains the phrase 'I find at my own mill...' which suggests that John Penn II had his own steam-driven mill.[7]

In February 1859 the families and the firm suffered a sad setback. William Hartree, partner in the firm, manager of the Greenwich works and brother-in-law to John Penn II died. He had been to Devonport dockyard dealing with a job on HMS *Windsor Castle*. On the Sunday evening train journey home the engine broke down in a tunnel and he offered to help overcome the problem. He spent two hours in the cold and damp tunnel and caught a chill which led to pleurisy. He died within days at the age of 45, leaving Charlotte and five children.[8] His funeral on the following Monday was conducted on a substantial scale. Charlotte bought a plot and had a family vault built in Nunhead Cemetery, some three miles from the family home (Area Map, p8). People lined the route for most of the way, shopkeepers closed as the procession went past and it was followed by about eight hundred men from the firm's works. The cortège consisted of the hearse drawn by six horses, preceded by pages and mutes and followed by six mourning carriages, each drawn

401 William Hartree, ca 1858

by four horses. These were followed by the carriages of the family and of friends. The service was held in the cemetery chapel.[9] The vault was a plain block with the inscription 'WILLIAM HARTREE, ENGINEER'. The title 'Engineer' gives a measure of the change that marriage and the firm brought about in his life, which he had started as a stationer. His Institution of Civil Engineers memoir tells that the loss would be most sincerely felt by all who had enjoyed the opportunity of appreciating the frankness and kind-heartedness of his character and his obituary in the *Kentish Mercury* states that he

> ...enjoyed the respect and esteem from a large circle of friends, and also the workmen generally in the employ of the firm.

He had strong literary interests and had formed a library of rather conventional material worth some £10,000.[10] He died intestate with his estate valued at 'less than £200,000'. William II, his eldest son, was then an apprentice at the firm.

During the same year John Penn II presented a paper on 'Superheated Steam in Marine Boilers' to the Institute of Mechanical Engineers.[11] In this he referred to the work of Thomas Howard with superheating and the Vaporising Engine and told of his close connection with Howard. He also contributed to a discussion on the construction of boilers. The firm provided an oscillating engine for a paddle steamer named *John Penn* [402, p52], built by Thames Iron Works & Shipbuilding Co

402 *John Penn*, cross channel packet

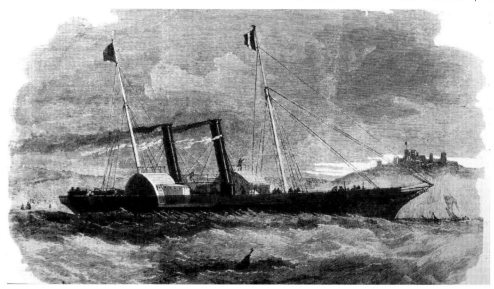

Steamboat Co. She quickly established a reputation as one of the fastest cross-channel mail packets and was chosen to convey both Russian and British royalty from Dover to Calais.[12]

From 1854 to 1859 the river scene from Penn's Deptford Works had been dominated by Brunel's great ship the *Great Eastern*, her building, the protracted launch at Millwall on the opposite bank and then her finishing whilst moored in Deptford reach. It had been a project fraught with difficulties and personal differences between Brunel the designer and John Scott Russell the builder which were well known and are still debated. After the completion of the finishing and once she had left the Thames, the owners, the Eastern Steam Navigation Company (ESN), claimed that the builder John Scott Russell had not completed the work according to the contract and withheld the final payment of £6,000. The issue went to arbitration and John Penn II, Joshua Field and others were called upon to act as expert witnesses.[13] The arbitrators found in favour of Russell to the amount of £18,000. ESN took the case to the Appeal Court and had a result in their favour. Russell then took the case to the Chief Justice and in 1861 the Appeal Court ruling was overturned. ESN eventually paid Russell the £18,000. This was the final chapter in the high-profile dispute which had involved Brunel (who died in 1859), the ESN, Russell and others. In 1860, when John Scott Russell was made secretary of the new Institution of Naval Architects John Penn II was one of the founder members.

During the Russian War the French navy had adopted a different approach to the design of ships for bombarding coastal defences than that of the British. They favoured larger battery ships heavily armoured with wrought-iron plate to withstand the fire of the shore batteries. After the end of the war they decided to construct an ironclad ship of the line and laid down *La Gloire* in 1858. Despite the recent allied status of Britain and France there was an immediate reaction by the British Admiralty. The traditional policy of superiority had to be maintained and a larger, more powerful, better-armed ship had to be built. The *Warrior* project was born.[14]

The Admiralty had their own design but requested design tenders from fifteen private and naval dockyards for comparison. Finally the Admiralty design for a thirty-four-gun, eight-thousand-ton, armoured frigate which could steam at thirteen and a half knots was chosen. The fact that the estimated cost of £250,000 was seven times that of a thirty-four-gun wooden sail frigate led to a great deal of argument about the project. The policy of outright superiority was upheld and contracts were placed with Thames Ironworks and Shipbuilding for the ship at £190,225 and with John Penn & Son for the machinery at £74,409. It was stipulated that the vessel should be launched in eleven months and ready, with machinery fitted, for completion with masts and rigging three months later. Penn's tender for trunk engines was slightly higher than Maudslay's for their reverse connecting engines but, with Penn's reputation for quality and reliability so well established in the Navy, his engines were preferred.

Warrior's whole design included many novel features and, as one might expect, building did not go as fast as planned. William Buchan was appointed Chief Engineer and spent time at Penn's works whilst the engines were being built; he had previously served in the sloop *Malacca*, which had Penn engines. The launch date had been set for April 1860, but this was not achieved. In September that year a very concerned Board of Admiralty visited the Thames Ironworks slipway and stopped the work whilst they deliberated. By that time *La Gloire* had been launched and had undergone successful trials. There was no real option but to continue with the project.

The Engineer reports the transfer of one of the engine cylinders from Penn's Greenwich works to Deptford for subsequent transfer by lighter to the vessel in January 1861.[15] The weight of the cylinder and the trailer was nearly eighty tons. Deptford Bridge [001, Area Map, p8] would have had temporary shoring to avoid damage by the heavy load. The road was icy and two traction engines were used. The article extols the virtues of traction engines for such a task. There was no comment that it would be preferable to have the production operations laid out so as to avoid the transfer altogether, as advocated by John Bourne in 1853.

In his 1861 5th edition of *Treatise on Steam*, Bourne, in a new passage, described *Warrior's* engines as

> ...the same form as the trunk engines for *Arrogant* and *Encounter* introduced several years ago for screw vessels...They are distinguished by the same beauty and accuracy of workmanship for which Messrs. Penn's engines have long been favoured.[16]

403 Trunk engine in Penn's works

In the main body of the book, probably taken from an earlier edition, he had commented

...we feel assured that these trunk engines will not possess very protracted vitality.[17]

Their vitality lasted into the 1870s. It is a pity he did not withdraw that comment from later editions.

HMS *Warrior's* launch was on 29 December 1860 and steam was raised for the first trial in February 1861. She sailed for Greenhithe in August, where the remaining work was completed, and finally sailed for Portsmouth in September of that year; John Penn II was on board. Sea trials showed better than design performance from the machinery with reservations only about the steering of the ship, especially at low speed.

404 HMS Warrior, engine room with visitors, 1861

With HMS *Warrior* (Plate IIIa), the first ironclad line-of-battle ship, Britain had regained her naval superiority. This was the second of John Penn & Son's Firsts. A 1990 survey of the ship's records states:

> Of particular note was the reliability of the main engines once initial deficiencies had been rectified and that boiler life was twice the hitherto norm. The former vindicates the choice of Penn's engines [Plate IIIb] and the latter that the assiduous attention to following the instructions for care of boilers was a major factor.[18]

From today's perspective it is interesting to see that even on this most modern ship, which had a donkey engine to work some of the pumps and the ash hoist, the work of raising the twenty-four-ton screw was done by four hundred men hauling on ropes. The time to set up the sheaves and lines for raising or lowering was one hour and twenty minutes. The raising or lowering time was about ten minutes.[19] This was possible on a naval ship with four hundred and fifty-five seamen, one hundred and eighteen marines and sixty-six stokers on board but the fact that there was no donkey-engined winch on deck shows the attitude of the Navy to the role of manpower. Another example of manual labour was coaling. Two hundredweight (one hundred kg) bags were loaded through the gunports and emptied down shoots to the bunkers. In a day only twenty-eight tons could be loaded. Two or more weeks' work were required to take on a normal loading.[20] Then the ship had to be scrubbed clean again.

In his book *Industrial Biography* (1863) Samuel Smiles wrote about the manufacture of the *Warrior's* engines.

The perfection of modern machine-tools is such that the utmost perfection is secured and the mechanical engineer can calculate on a degree of exactitude that does not admit of a deviation beyond the thousandth part of an inch. When the powerful oscillating engines of the Warrior were put on board the ship, the parts, consisting of some five thousand pieces, were brought from their different workshops of the Messrs. Penn and Sons, where they had been made by workmen who knew not the places they were to occupy, and fitted together with such precision that so soon as the steam was raised and let into the cylinders, the immense machine began as if to breathe and move like a living creature. Stretching its huge arms like a new-born giant, and then, after practising its strength a little and proving its soundness in body and limb, it started off with the power of above a thousand horses to try its strength in breasting the billows of the North Sea.[21]

This shows a rather naïve understanding of engineering but gives a clear sense of his feelings (I cannot match my great-great grandfather's literary style – RH).

Another, rather bizarre, compliment to Penn's *Warrior* engines was a very miniature model. It stood on a baseplate smaller than a 5p piece with three-millimetre-diameter cylinders. It worked admirably, turning at a very high speed. It was made by a Mr Smith and was, in 1875, in the possession of John Penn II.[22]

The Navy had further ironclads built in the 1860s and many were fitted with the preferred Penn trunk engines. HMS *Warrior*, beautifully restored and fitted with replica Penn trunk engines and boilers, is an important part of the Portsmouth Historic Dockyard museum complex and is open for public visits. These replicas are the only full-size, turning but not really working, Penn trunk engines which can be seen. No originals have survived in working condition. This is the fate of most marine engines, which are usually scrapped with the rest of the ship. There are very few to see compared with railway locomotives and stationary engines.

405 John Penn II,
Joseph Whitworth, Robert Napier,
William Fairbairn.
Presidents of the Institution of
Mechanical Engineers.
Manchester Meeting 1866

One of the other ironclads with Penn engines was HMS *Black Prince*. She was built in 1861 on the Clyde by R. Napier and was one of very few Penn-engined ships not built on Thameside or by naval dockyards. Robert Napier would have been known to John Penn through the Institution of Mechanical Engineers. The firm invited five hundred people on board for a trial run in the Clyde estuary. They had a sumptuous dinner on board with John Penn II in the chair.[23] At the time of *Warrior's* commissioning in 1861 the situation of naval Chief and Senior Engineers had not changed. They still had wardroom, but not yet military or command, status. They were outside the ship's chain of command and discipline in spite of the fact that they were responsible for her fighting power source and, on HMS *Warrior*, an engine room complement of ten officers plus eighty-three petty officers and men which made up an eighth of the total complement. The Navy, like many organisations, was finding social change much more difficult than technical development. It was in this year that William Penn, John II's uncle, died at the age of 89.

406 William Penn, ca1858

The large new house at The Cedars allowed John Penn II to enjoy making a collection of works of art. There are records of purchases of pictures from the artist Frank Stone in 1856 and 1858, also of purchases from galleries from 1860 to 1870. Prices ranged from less than £100 to £885. A major purchase, in about 1860, was of a marble statue of Pandora by the English sculptor J. Gibson, who lived in Rome. Penn wrote to him:

> …I have today paid to Messrs Baring Brothers £700 – of which no doubt they will inform you – I assure you I like the Pandora very much it is like all your productions, universally admired…[24]

The *Athenaeum* critic made a rather different judgement.

> Mr. Gibson whose execution is fair enough, painfully labours to galvanise the spirit of an epoch which must be for ever dead to us…Nothing but the superficial finish keeps the student's taste from revolting at the attempt to reproduce Greek Art so laboriously – clutched, indeed, rather than felt.[25]

In a second letter to Gibson, John Penn wrote:

> …I quite agree with you that it should not be placed in the greenhouse I am getting a temporary stand made to place it for the present in the drawing room. When you come to London next year you can advise me where you would like it best…

407 Marble bust of
John Penn II,
by Papworth, 1864

408 The Cedars, drawing room,
Pandora statue by the window

There is a later photograph of the drawing room at The Cedars showing Pandora. The statue is now in the Victoria & Albert Museum in South Kensington. It was presented by William Penn's widow in 1922. The family records show that his picture collection included a small Turner and a Landseer. John Penn II was a genuine collector with rather conventional tastes.

Two other archived copies of letters show John Penn II undertaking a small professional role personally rather than as a member of the firm.[26] A George Fletcher was being forced to move from his works in Southwark and needed a figure for the compensation he should expect. John Penn II suggested two people as valuers and then carefully examined their report before recommending that their figure of £5,925 was a fair amount for compensation. It is most probable he would have done many things like this. An illustration of the breadth of his interests and his local standing comes from his position as the first president of the West Kent Microscopical Society in 1859.[27]

The 1861 census gives a little view of life at The Cedars, with John and Ellen Penn and their six children – John (13), William (11), Frank (9), Ellen (8), Alfred (6) and Isabella (4) – and five house servants, four nurses and a governess all living in the house. There would also have been garden and stable staff. Charlotte Hartree at Morden Hill had a smaller establishment with children William (19), engineering apprentice, John Penn (16), Isabella (15), Louisa (13) and Charles (10), all scholars, and four house servants.

During the 1860s and into the 1870s The Cedars was a centre for Blackheath social life. The summer *fêtes champetres* were major events, especially for the young.[28] The Penns also hosted the annual fetes of the Blackheath Horticultural Society. In 1861 John Penn II made a second postnuptial settlement for Ellen. There would be one more in 1865. It is important to remember that these and marriage settlements were the only way a wife could hold property independent of her husband. He may well have wished to be sure of her situation if the firm should get into financial trouble and may have wished to enable her to carry out and be seen to carry out charitable work independently.

The Admiralty's recommendation about engine suppliers gave rise to mixed views in the ship-building and engineering trades. In 1861 the shipbuilder Laird of Birkenhead wrote to *The Times* on the subject which, in turn, led to an editorial in *The Engineer*.[29] The Admiralty practice of us-ing only approved suppliers for engines was not applied to the building of ships. Less qualified yards could put in low-priced bids and fail to supply the quality. Laird, seeing himself as a quality shipbuilder, criticised the absence of a similar recommendation for ships because it resulted in unfair competition for the quality yards and poor-quality ships being delivered. He then criticised the engine supply arrangement but in this case because it made it too difficult for an outsider to become approved, as approval was based on jobs done. He claimed that this situation had enabled Penn to expand in the certainty of getting work; that is, to invest with no risk. It seems as though Laird wanted to have things both ways.

The International Exhibition at South Kensington was held in 1862, and the firm exhibited ma-rine engines in the General Machinery section. Possibly associated with the exhibition a group of Japanese ambassadors visited the works of John Penn & Son accompanied by Mr Lloyd, engineer-in-chief to the Navy.[30] In the morning they vis-ited the Greenwich works where they showed great interest in the Nasmyth steam hammers and asked to see the pouring of molten iron into moulds. After two hours they went by car-riage to The Cedars for luncheon and visited Deptford in the afternoon, departing for Lon-don at three o'clock on the yacht owned by the firm, accompanied by Thomas and young Frank Penn. The firm had supplied engines for vessels sent to Japan in 1853 and 1856; the next order was in 1877.

409 Thomas Penn, ca1858

Also in 1862 John Penn II again asked John Hedges if he would return to be with the firm in England. There had been a reorganisation in Mannheim which might have been a reason to return. Possibly John Penn was anxious to in-crease his management strength after the loss of William Hartree. John Hedges declined; his daughter was by then married to a local man and had a family which Hedges and his wife did not wish to leave.[31] The Hedges story shows how John Penn II cared for, respected and kept in touch with one of his father's men. Hedges died in 1870.

In 1863 the firm provided an oscillating engine for the *Alberta*, a paddle yacht which acted as a tender to the Royal Yacht *Victoria and Albert I*. Penn's involvement in Royal Yachts is an interest-ing case of the strength of the firm's reputation. In Victoria's reign several yachts and tenders were built. The first was the *Victoria and Albert I* (1843–55) of 420 tons, a paddle yacht with sails. In 1855 her name was changed to *Osborne* and she was paid off in 1859; her engines were by Maudslay.

Then there was the Tender *Fairy* (1845–68) of 18 tons, the screw-propelled yacht described earlier, with engines by Penn. Another Tender was the *Elfin* (1849–1901) of 40 tons, a paddle-wheel yacht with sails, and engines by Rennie. She was used for the Portsmouth to Isle of Wight service associated with the Queen's regular trips to Osborne. Then there was the Royal Yacht *Victoria and Albert II* (1855–1901) of 350 tons, a paddle yacht with sails and Penn oscillating engines. She was followed by the Tender *Alberta* (1863–1913) of 33 tons, a paddle yacht with sails and Penn engines and finally the Royal Yacht *Osborne II* (1868–1908) of 200 tons, a paddle yacht with sails, and engines by Maudslay.[32] At times there was a little flotilla of three vessels, used for different purposes. Paddle ships dominated as these vessels were for coastal rather than ocean-going service.

In 1863 there was a Royal visit to the Greenwich and Deptford works. A letter from Major Elphinstone, the Royal Princes' governor, dated 17 February 1863 to Queen Victoria tells that

> Prince Arthur...This afternoon will visit the large factories of Messrs John Penn who supply the engines to the Royal Yachts and to most of our men of war.[33]

This may not be factually quite correct but it illustrates the firm's reputation.

The consequence of this Royal involvement was that John Penn & Son received orders from foreign royalty for the engines for their yachts. After all, as rulers of nations without advanced technical capabilities, who should they emulate other than the ruler of the leading maritime empire? Thus we find the yachts of the Emperors of Russia and Austria, the Khedive of Egypt and the Sultan of the Ottoman Empire all with engines by Penn. It was good business, quality rather than price sensitive. In 1864 John Penn II acquired a steam paddle yacht *Lara* for his own personal use. She was built by Samuda and fitted with a Penn oscillating engine.

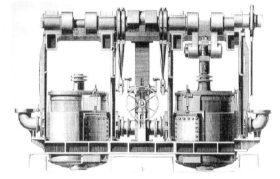

410 Oscillating engine for Bosphorus steamer, 1860s

Similar considerations applied to nations which wished to build up their own navies. They came to Britain to place their orders. The supply of Penn engines to the navies of Russia, Italy, Spain, Brazil, Germany, Peru and Japan has already been mentioned. In the 1860s and 70s orders also came from China, Egypt, Chile, Holland and Denmark.[34] In the 1870s an engineer from the firm, George Kinsey, went to install engines in Holland, Italy and Romania.[35] Foreign orders also came for engines in commercial vessels for steam navigation companies in Russia, Turkey, on the Nile, off the cost of Guiana and elsewhere. Many of these were for oscillating engines, robust machines which gave long service with simple maintenance. This is well illustrated by the Elbe steamers. The *Bohemia/Diesbar* was mentioned in Chapter 2. Another striking example was the *John Penn*, a passenger paddle steamer of 1864 with a Penn oscillating engine. She was still operating at the outbreak of World War II when, for patriotic reasons, her name was changed to *Herrnskretschen*, a local place name. She was sunk in the Dresden raids of 1945, raised, repaired and transferred to Czechoslovakian ownership as post-war reparations. She was renamed *Freundschaft-Pratelistvi* and continued in service, with the original Penn oscillating engine until 1966; she was 'eine legende auf der Elbe'.[36] [411, p60]

411 *John Penn*, Elbe steamer, built 1864 - 'eine legende auf der Elbe'

In the summer of 1863 John Penn II was one of those present at gunnery trials at Shoeburyness. Trials of competing gun and projectile designs were important in this period of competition be-tween defensive armour plate and aggressive artillery. John Penn II's reputation and standing as a major supplier to the Admiralty would have warranted his presence there.[37]

In 1865 Maudslay, Sons & Field acquired a property in East Greenwich, on the west-facing shore of the Greenwich peninsula. It was quite large and enabled them to enter the shipbuilding busi-ness and to concentrate boilermaking there.[38] Their Lambeth site was very congested and incon-venient. This shows that sites with better location than that of Penn's at Greenwich were available locally. It was at this time that the last Thames-built passenger liners and mail steamers were com-pleted. From the data available about the firm's orders this would not have been a big loss, as their business did not include engines for ocean liners, but it should have been seen as an indicator of the trend in the industry.

A near neighbour in Blackheath was Samuel Smiles, well known as an author but at the time working as the Secretary of the South East Railway. He would go up to town every day by train, return in the evening and, after being with the family, would retire to his study to write. He was a self-made man, born in Haddington, had put himself through medical school in Edinburgh, tried to set up in practice as a doctor around Haddington and then in Leeds, realised the only patients he could get were ones who could not pay, and so went into journalism. He edited a Leeds paper, became a railway company secretary in Leeds and then moved to London to be Secretary of the S.E. Railway. Success as an author came to him in the early 1860s with his *Life of George Stephenson* and with *Self Help*, a collection of short biographies of self-made men. The field of engineering was rich with self-made men and he followed the George Stephenson book with *Lives of the Engineers*, *Industrial Biography*, *Invention and Industry* and many more, all written in his spare time. In 1863 John Penn II provided help to Samuel Smiles for *Industrial Biography*, especially for the section on Joseph Clement, whom John Penn had known well.[39]

"My dear Sir,

I will "Rub up" the information about the Warrior Engines and send it to you. I also send to-day the Record of the International Exhibition in which you will see a notice of Bramah and Maudslay. I think I understood you had seen or are about to see Mr Field.

I remain

Yours truly

John Penn

S. Smiles Esq."

412 Letter from John Penn II to Samuel Smiles

Smiles had used his earnings from his hobby-writing to build a new house above the Hartrees' home at Morden Hill. John Penn (Jack) Hartree, the second son, was studying natural sciences at Cambridge. Janet Smiles, the elder daughter, had returned home after looking after her younger brother who was living in Bradford. She was a very vivacious and sociable girl who had earlier, with an elder brother, attended a masked ball at Mansion House using their parents' tickets. As a reward for doing her family duty for the younger brother the Smiles parents took Janet on holiday to Switzerland, accompanied by her younger sister and the very shy and retiring Jack Hartree. After their return the Smiles went to visit the Hartree family and chat about the shared holiday. The quiet, reserved Jack Hartree used the occasion to announce that he and Janet were engaged. His mother's reaction to this news was awful. She claimed that the holiday had been set up by the Smiles on purpose so that Janet could benefit from the inheritance Jack would receive at age twenty-one. No one else in the room, including Jack, knew of it. The allegation was totally in opposition to Smiles's position that wealth should be earned by hard work, as described in *Self Help* and exemplified in all his writings, and that wealth by inheritance was almost an evil. Her words were deeply offensive to the Smiles family. Jack broke into tears. Remembering that Charlotte would have seen her father working hard to earn the money it is understandable that she would have felt very protective towards it, but that cannot excuse her insensitivity to her guests' principles. Jack finished his Cambridge studies with a first-class degree and went on to study medicine. He and Janet were married in 1868. For ever after the Smiles family thought of Charlotte Hartree's home as a rather boring place.[40]

In the years 1863, 65 and 67 there were three very different visits to the factories of John Penn & Son for which the reports are still available. They provide good insights into the firm's working.

The first was by P. Barry, who would now be described as an investigative journalist. He had taken on a mission to expose the deplorable state of the Admiralty-operated naval dockyards, which he

413 Staff at Penn's Works

414 Staff at Penn's Works

believed were totally unsuited to prepare the Navy in readiness for war. For his investigation he visited naval dockyards and private firms in Britain, France and the USA. A major weakness of the Admiralty dockyards was in the line management. There were some very technically competent civil employees but the dockyard management was staffed by commissioned military officers who had come to the end of their line of promotion at sea and were given these jobs as sinecures. They had no experience of industrial management yet were placed in control of large industrial establishments. Jobbery, pilferage and other loss-making practices were deeply engrained in the dockyard culture. Barry believed the only way to cure this was to close the dockyards and have private industry take over their role. In his book *Dockyard Economy and Naval Power* he gives accounts of all his visits. His mission needs to be borne in mind when reading them. John Penn & Son receive the longest account, the most photographs and the most praise of the many firms he visited. A quotation is worthwhile.

> Foremost in tradition, name and magnitude, not only in this country but in the world. France has no such engineering works, neither does America. Together they are equal to the whole engineering needs of the Royal Navy, in the greatest possible extremity. This is a fact, the suggestiveness and importance of which could scarcely be overrated. As may be readily supposed, the works of John Penn & Son are a model of economic adaptation and administrative skill. Complete efficiency is attained by vesting skilled foremen with a great amount of power and holding them responsible for its proper exercise. Into the hands of the foremen the work to be done is committed under the supervision of members of the firm, and the foremen may on the instant discharge workmen for shortcomings or misconduct. The foremen, in point of fact, are the masters of the workmen, and, on entering and leaving the works with the workmen are never at a loss; nor is there any opportunity, even if there is a will, to be idle or imperfect in the performance of the appointed tasks. This is the secret of the faultless engines; engines which will do their work without breakdown, as long as coal and water were supplied, and indifferently in smooth or troubled water. Upon the best cast and forged metal the best workmanship is placed. And, to do Penn's workforce justice, the yoke of supervision is an easy, nay, a pleasant one. Treated as men always deserve to be treated, the great body of them have attained that frame of mind which identifies their employers' interests as their own. An enquirer in Greenwich or Deptford will find that Penn's 'men' are a class known to and esteemed by the whole community, chiefly because of the respect they manifest for themselves and for the esteem in which they hold the members of the firm. The distinguished foreign gentlemen who from time to time have taken off their coats at Penn's works to become practically conversant with marine engine building, no doubt look back on the time of intelligent association with Penn's workmen. The superior administrative staff is small, which is another suggestive circumstance. Two or three able men, even in engine building, easily direct a thousand. The argument is unanswerable against numerous staffs, and particularly where work is less exact and skilled than in engine building. It is also unanswerable against large outlays for more control. A description of these great national works is not required. Sufficient to say that the boiler shop, erecting shop, turnery, foundry, forge etc. are unsurpassed.[41]

Even with Barry's mission borne in mind this is an impressive account of the way Penn's works operated and his stress on the interpersonal relations confirms the effectiveness of Penn's approach to 'his men'. It is a pity that there is no mention of the design staff who were also key to the firm's success. He also does not seem to have been aware of any commercial or administrative staff. The only engineering comment is the observation that there were Whitworth machine tools in the works.

415 Foundry at Penn's Greenwich works, 1863

416 Heavy Turnery at Penn's Greenwich works, John Penn II facing camera, 1863

The second visit, reported in *The Illustrated London News* of 7 October 1865, opens with a telling passage.

> We published, in the *Illustrated London News* of Oct. 15, 1864, a series of illustrations of the great locomotive manufactory of Messrs. Stephenson, at Newcastle. This establishment was chosen from amongst the other great workshops of England, not because it was the largest or most important, but because it was the most intimately associated with the early history of the locomotive engine and the introduction of the railway system. On the same principle we have selected for the subject of our present Illustrations the great manufactory of Messrs. Penn, as one which will best exemplify the progress of the construction of marine engines.

418 Turning a steam engine crankshaft, 1865

417 Penn's Greenwich works, Heavy Turnery, 1865

Penn would have been proud of the association with the name of Stephenson, but to be chosen for his place in history rather than his importance would have been a bit hard. There follows a brief history of steam navigation and of the firm and outline descriptions of the works at Greenwich and Deptford. The Greenwich works are described as

> ...constructed upon the most modern approved plans. Every part of each shop is fully lighted in every direction, and the machinery and tools combine the most recent improvements. The premises cover seven acres of ground, and in them are employed 1300 men and boys.

Castings of up to 30 tons were made in the foundry. At Deptford about 500 hands were employed and some 1500 tons of wrought-iron plate used annually. There is a delightful description of the pouring of molten metal into the moulds in the foundry.

> The pouring of so large a mass of metal equally into the mould is a most important matter, and is executed by the principal founder, for irregularity or too quick running the metal would not only spoil the casting, but might endanger the lives of those present.

This ends with

> ...while the bright glow of the molten iron, almost white in its intense heat, lights up the features and forms of the workmen and numerous visitors in a wondrous manner; for at such times, not only are the visitors numerous, but all the younger hands of the establishment contrive to find their way into the foundry; and so do many of the old ones, for the hearts of the men, as well as those of the masters, must be in the work of a factory such as this.

Safety concerns were very different in those days. It seems that neither Barry nor the writer of this report were able to look at what they saw with the eyes of an engineer.

420 Penn's Greenwich Works, Foundry, 1865

An interesting insight into the kind of practical difficulties arising from the firm's site location comes in a report in *The Times* of 4 September 1866 about transporting the thirty-five-ton forging for the crankshaft of the engine for HMS *Hercules* from the forge on Merseyside to Greenwich. The London and North Western Railway had only one flatbed wagon which could take the weight, and it was not immediately available. The rail journey was limited to ten miles per hour and could take place only on Sundays to avoid interference with traffic. Once arrived at Camden Town station Pickfords took over the job. The load, 'the terrible shaft', was banned from crossing the new Westminster Bridge and watchmen were placed to ensure it was not 'smuggled over'. Drawn by thirty horses the shaft, weighing forty tons on its trolley, left Camden Town at 6.00am. It passed down Regent Street and Waterloo Place followed by a crowd of curious sightseers all the way. They held their breath with concern that the brakes might not hold and it would crash into the Guards Monument. It passed over the underground railway, across Waterloo Bridge, then two railway bridges at New Cross, holding up rail traffic as it went, and on down to Deptford Bridge which had been braced by the firm in their accustomed way for heavy loads. It makes a good story but everything added to the costs of making the engine.

The third visit, reported in *The Engineer* of 20 September 1867, was made by the Society of Engineers. It first reports that the party arrived at the factory lunch hour, so the members dispersed in the town in search of refreshment and returned to reassemble. During the visit they had free run of the Greenwich works. The first feature reported is that the factory is a considerable distance from the river so the firm had to bear the cost of hauling their heavy products through the streets from Greenwich to Deptford. The main erecting shop is described as

> ...roofed in timber and old-fashioned in get up and arrangement,...still so large and lofty that it affords ample accommodation for a very extensive business.

Then there is a description of the work in progress on the massive engines for the *Hercules* and reference is made to the transport of the crankshaft across London. There is a full description of a special machine tool made by Penn for the finishing of crankshafts. It was an object of wonder and shows the inventive way in which the firm approached its work. Another example was a special shaping machine. They saw engines for steam launches being assembled in a fitting shop and were impressed by the facilities for grinding cutting tools by the use of a template to ensure uniformity of cutting angle, in contrast to relying on manual skill (This practice could have been an innovation introduced by John Penn I). The stables which housed draught horses for moving heavy equipment in the works and through the streets were praised. In this context it can be noted that John Penn II is reputed to have said, when talking about the selection of the best men:

> It is easier to arrive at a satisfactory conclusion on the qualities of a horse than a man.

The steam engines providing power are described. Also mentioned is the private electric telegraph which connected the two works; later this was extended to The Cedars. Towards the end of the account is the passage:

> The remarkable excellence of Messrs. Penn's machinery does not depend on the performance of magnificent machine tools. Tools there are in plenty, all good of their kind, but nearly all old fashioned. We must seek for Mr Penn's success in his own talent and the skill of his men. None but first-class hands are employed, and no piece-work is done in any department of the estab-

lishment. Intelligence and manual skill can, under proper arrangements, do much more than any tools. It is certain, at least, that inferior workmen with the best possible tools will produce inferior work. Mr Penn and his partners have evidently carefully borne this fact in mind – the civilised world knows with what results.

There is also an account of an American marine engine which was designed to be of similar power to the engine Penn made for HMS *Sappho*. The American engine weighed sixty tons more than that for the *Sappho*, which itself weighed less than sixty tons. Here was a good example of the importance of design skills and a tribute to Penn and his designers.

This is a better-informed engineering assessment of Penn's works and brings out the special value of their skilled workforce once again. It is interesting that, at this time of quite rapid machine tool development, the inferior workmen argument is introduced almost as though to support the firm's low level of investment in new machine tools. It also suggests that Penn's expansion, referred to in Laird's 1861 letter to *The Times*, did not involve any notable new machinery. It had involved the purchase of the land west of the footpath in 1860 and of the original Greenwich site in 1862. The firm built new millwrights' and carpenters' shops, stables and stores on the lower level but it was not until after the Penns' time that the space was fully used. The land purchase committed the firm even more strongly to the Greenwich location. In 1867 John Penn II was made an honorary member of the Society of Engineers. John Penn II and this visit were remembered again in *The Engineer* with two 'Sixty Years Ago' articles in 1938.[42]

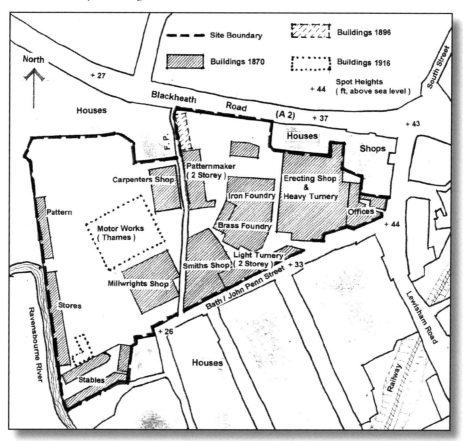

420 Layout of Greenwich Engine Works

5. THE COMING OF THE COMPOUND AND THE END OF AN ERA (1867–1878)

It was during the 1860s that the use of compound engines started to become established for marine use. For efficient operation higher boiler pressures were required than those previously used for simple condensing engines and their successful application required many developments in design, manufacturing and materials. In 1861 HMS *Warrior*, with jet condensing engines, had operated at 20 psi and by 1865 HMS *Bellerophon,* with surface condensing engines, was operating at 30 psi. Compound engines operated at up to about twice these pressures. In a compound the steam was used first in a high-pressure and then in a low-pressure cylinder; thus the pressure of the steam at the end of the first expansion was not wasted but was used in the second. Hence the compound was more efficient and it became economically attractive for ocean routes where coal was expensive. Local supplies of coal were rare and coal had to be shipped to ports acting as coaling stations. This was done in sailing ships which were the cheapest way for bulk cargo; the application of the new technology was dependent on the old, as is often the case.

An important step had been taken by the Pacific Steam Navigation Company in 1855 with the fitting two of its new vessels with compound engines. Their success encouraged them to bring home and refit three other vessels. In 1863 the P&O adopted compounds for new construction. Humphreys, Tennant & Dykes supplied the engine for the *Carnatic*. This was so successful that by 1866 P&O had ten compound-engined vessels in its fleet. Then, in 1865, the Navy fitted a compound engine into the wooden frigate HMS *Constance*. She was raced from Plymouth to Madeira against sister ships *Arethusa* and *Octavia* with Penn trunk and Maudslay reverse connecting rod engines. All three ran out of coal but *Constance* had the lowest coal consumption, which showed the compound's advantage of greater efficiency. The subsequent introduction of compound engines into the Navy eventually led to the end of the Penn dominance in the supply of engines of large horsepower. However, the firm's trunk engines continued to be chosen for the big naval ships into the 1870s because of their proven reliability.

Writers on the Thameside shipbuilding industry tell of the effects on the industry of the collapse of the Overend Gurney Bank in 1866. There are differences amongst their conclusions about the importance of this event to the industry. It caused the collapse of the shipbuilders Millwall Ironworks and the short-lived firm of James Ash, both of which had been, in effect, owned by Overend Gurney, and it deeply affected London Engineering and Iron Shipbuilding who were active in iron fabrication as well as shipbuilding and who went into liquidation on 1871. These failures would not have affected the demand for new vessels and there is no evidence that this banking collapse had an important effect on the local marine engineering business.

Penn's British patent 2114 for the lignum vitae propeller stern tube bearings was based on a sound claim and the royalties were a significant source of income. Licensed shipbuilders or marine engineers either paid the royalty or had the owners or operators of the ship pay it directly to Penn. There was one incidence of refusal to pay and Penn could not afford to let it go unchallenged. In January 1866 he took it to court in the case Penn vs Bibby; Jack; Fernie.[1] It was heard in the Vice Chancellor's Court. The Vice Chancellor found for Penn but the defendants requested a retrial before the Lord Chancellor. In December 1867 the case came before the Lord Chancellor. He said the questions of fact before the court were: 1) Was the invention new at the time of the patent? Bibby etc. claimed that wood bearings had been used earlier in millwork. 2) Was the specification sufficient? 3) Was the invention the subject matter of a patent? 4) Had the defendants infringed? The Lord Chancellor stated that the Vice Chancellor was justified in finding in favour of the novelty, the specification and the subject matter. Infringement had taken place. Costs would go to Penn. There was a question of damages. Penn had licensed others to make the bearings at a royalty of 2s 6d per horsepower and that amount was clearly due to him. He also claimed lost profit on the manufacture and installation of the bearings. The court did not accept that claim because, as he had licensed other firms, it could not be assumed he would have manufactured these. A sum of £2005:15s:4d had already been paid by the owners of some of the vessels concerned and this would be taken into account when determining the royalty settlement. The final amount of damages is not reported.

There were two drawbacks to the use of screw ships for coastal service. One was the problem of sand and grit entering the stern bearing and the other was the large diameter of the propellers, which made a really shallow draught impossible. No satisfactory theory of propeller design was available at the time, largely because the concept of the curved aerofoil blade had not been realised, so larger diameters were seen as the way to increase thrust. Paddle ships continued to be used for river and coastal service well into the 1900s. The firm continued to supply engines – oscillating and, later, compound – for these vessels.

In 1866–8 John Penn was again elected President of the Institution of Mechanical Engineers. During this presidency he used his contacts in Paris, General Morin and others, to arrange for the Institute's annual conference to be held in conjunction with the 1867 Paris International Exhibition.[2] The firm exhibited the trunk engines built for, but never fitted in, HMS *Sappho*. According to John Bourne they

> ...left all other competitors far behind. Their finish, their symmetry and their simplicity, attracted the attention of all competent observers, and of Mr. Penn himself, who was there at the time, it was observed that his merit was only excelled by his modesty.

The engines won a prize for their simplicity and elegance of design.[3]

John Penn II's modesty is shown again in the simple fact that his daily commute was a walk of just over a mile from The Cedars down to the works and back up again, a practice which he maintained as long as his health permitted and after which it became a ride in his bath chair. At the end of his second period as President of the Institution of Mechanical Engineers he presented the library with a 1792 copy of Bugeron's *Manual de Tourneur*.[4]

In 1865 the firm had had a different kind of contract. In the previous year the *Great Eastern* had been converted into a cable-laying ship in order to lay the first transatlantic telegraph cable.[5] The attempt failed when a break occurred some five hundred miles off the Newfoundland coast and the installed equipment was not strong enough to raise the broken cable from the ocean floor. For the 1866 attempt both the laying and picking-up machinery were redesigned and replaced. John Penn and Son provided the picking-up equipment. The engines used for both laying and picking up were non-condensing trunk engines operating at low pressure from the ship's boilers.

In 1866 a new cable was successfully laid and the broken one picked-up, spliced and completed. In a contribution to the discussion of a paper at the Institution of Mechanical Engineers John Penn II, then President, commented on the special features which were included in the equipment to avoid sudden strains on the cable, including the installation of a large safety valve close to the engine's valve chest.[6]

Great Eastern had originally been fitted with a stern bearing of white metal pads supported on large iron blocks. After her initial Atlantic return crossing the white metal on the bottom pads had completely worn away and repair or replacement was necessary. Joshua Field described his inspection with John Penn.[7] They recommended that the bottom blocks should be removed and modified to lignum vitae pads bearing the load as in Penn's patent design. These were fitted, without removing the propeller shaft, and gave satisfactory performance for the rest of her service life.

At this time there was growing concern about boiler explosions, especially because of the higher steam pressure used for compound engines. Explosions which caused deaths would always be the subject of a coroner's inquest. Whilst recognising the reason for this the engineers felt that the coroners' courts were not properly qualified to establish the cause of explosions and were concerned about the intended legislation. William Fairbairn made a strong plea against legislation.

> In this country we are always jealous of the Government interference, in matters relating to industrial projects or individuals in their single or collective capacity, and for two reasons; firstly that official inspection is not always judicious; and, secondly that it removes the responsibilities off the shoulders of those who ought to bear it.[8]

This is rather stronger than our objections to regulation today. The subject was taken up by the British Association for the Advancement of Science in 1868 and a committee of Fairbairn, Whitworth, Penn and others was set up to consider

> ...how far coroners' inquisitions are satisfactory tribunals for the investigation of boiler explosions and how these tribunals might be improved.

Once again, John Penn II was acting as a member of the engineering establishment.

In 1867 John Matthew, partner and Chief Designer of the firm, retired. He had by then gone to live in London where one of his activities was as an amateur fireman. He would put on the Metropolitan Fire Brigade uniform and help at emergencies. He had a collection of fire brigade memorabilia as well as his workshop and telescope at his Park Lane house. Sadly he became ill within a year and died in 1869.[9] His will was valued at 'less than £350,000'. His daughter Bessie inherited Burford Lodge after her mother's death. She and her husband made many improvements there.

John Penn III, eldest son of John Penn II, had been to Harrow School in 1863–5 and then to Trinity College, Cambridge.[10] After that he became an apprentice in the family firm. He took his future responsibilities in the firm seriously and made sure he had some practical training and experience. In 1870 he registered a patent relating to a method of forming plates into shapes suitable to make curved pipes.[11] His younger brother William was at Harrow from 1865 to 1867; there is no record of his further education.

The period 1866 to 1886 is known as 'The Long Slump' for shipbuilding.[12] There was a large fall in the amount of shipbuilding nationwide between 1866 and 1867. On the Thames it fell to less than half. This caused a major change in the business conditions for the firm. The changes can be seen from the data of Appendix 2, p118. Between those years the annual number of vessels for which the firm supplied engines fell from twenty-nine to fourteen, which is similar to the drop for the Thames business as a whole. In 1868 the number is back up to sixteen but in each of the next three years it was down in single figures.[13] Business was very weak.

1868 saw the launch of the third ship to be named *John Penn*. She was a twin screw merchant ferry ordered from Australia. She worked between New South Wales and New Zealand and was wrecked off the coast of NSW in 1879. The wreck has been found and the two twin-cylinder crosshead engines and boiler sketched.[14]

The Franco-Prussian War and the defeat of France in 1870 saw the collapse of Napoleon III's empire and his capture by the Prussians. In September that year his son and the Empress Eugenie fled to England and settled in Chislehurst, Kent. The ex-Emperor joined them in early 1871. It was his third exile in England.

In 1871 the firm made its third First for the Navy. This was the supply of the engines for HMS *Devastation*, the first mastless battleship; that is, with no sails, propelled by steam only (Plate IIb).[15] She had twin turrets mounting her main guns and actually had masts to carry her signal flags. Two sets of trunk engines, operating at only 30 psi, were fitted to drive twin propellers. Improvements in design and manufacturing led to the price of the machinery for *Devastation*, £63,188, being lower than that for *Warrior* ten years earlier even though she had twin screws and greater power. It is curious to note that only two years before the first mastless ship of the line, a Particular Squadron of four steam frigates and two steam corvettes made a circumnavigation of the globe entirely under sail as an exercise in seamanship.[16] It was a kind of last fling of the seamanship school in the Navy. Despite *Devastation*'s complete dependence on steam the Navy's engineer officers continued to be denied command status.

The firm's concentration on marine engines did not exclude other work during this period of slump. A different project that year was the supply of the engines for the first organ in the Royal Albert Hall. This was the second set of organ engines supplied by the firm, those for the Alexandra Palace coming a bit earlier.[17] The Albert Hall's was a great organ, claimed to be the finest in the world.[18] It was made by Willis of Camden Town, who had already built the organs for St George's Hall, Liverpool, and for the Alexandra Park Crystal Palace. John Penn & Son provided two horizontal engines to provide the wind for the pipes and a vertical beam engine to power the compressed air for the operation of the valves and stops from the keyboard. These continued in use until 1920 when electrically driven rotary blowers were installed. The beam engine is in the Science Museum collection at the Wroughton store. The organ was, and still is, a very conspicuous feature of the hall. The opening ceremony was brought forward at the request of Queen Victoria and the organ was not quite complete, so the critics' comments on the opening concert were more concerned with the acoustics of the hall and the excessive reverberation which had been somewhat subdued by a large awning spread beneath the roof.

> ...but it is still evident that the hall is adapted rather for vast effects from a large number than for the minuter delicacies of performance.

This still holds true. Saint-Saëns is reputed to have said:

> The bellows of the gigantic organ at the Albert Hall in London worked by a steam engine thus guaranteeing the player an inexhaustible supply of air but at the same time eliminating all possibilities of unforeseen incidents.[19]

The organ was refurbished again in 2004 and the 1920s electric drive replaced.

A more unlikely project was in cooperation with the Aeronautical Society of Great Britain. At a meeting of the Society in 1870 the President, Sir William Fairbairn, drew attention to the fact that there was no data giving the 'reactions and lifting forces on inclined flat surfaces in wind'. It was resolved to carry out a programme of experiments to determine these forces. These were carried out in the works of John Penn & Son at Greenwich in the following year.[20] A wind tunnel had been designed by the Society's researchers and was built by the firm, who also provided the steam-driven air supply. Fans were quite a normal part of their business as they were installed for boiler room ventilation and for forced draught. Four different-shaped flat plates were used in the experiments. The sample plates were mounted on a horizontal arm with a counterbalance weight. The upward thrust on the plate would push down the other end of the arm and the force could be measured by a spring steelyard. The experiments established that the lift was proportional to the sine of the angle of the plate to the wind direction. These were the very first attempts to gain quantitative knowledge of these aerodynamic forces and were subject to the limitations of the apparatus. At the time it was not appreciated that a curved plate is required to generate the lift of an aerofoil.

Another story from this period concerns James Starley (1830–81), who as a young man worked as a gardener at The Cedars.[21] He had a very inventive mind and, unaided, repaired Mrs Penn's sewing machine. John Penn II recognised his ability and arranged an apprenticeship for him with the manufacturer, who was a personal friend. Starley later moved to Coventry and in the 1860s took out patents with the Coventry Sewing Machine Co.[22] He then became involved in the manufacture of velocipedes and took out several patents related to these and, as the name changed, to bicycles. A very important one, in 1870, was a design for a tension-spoked wheel which was the precursor to the bicycle wheel of today. He brought out the Ariel bicycle, which was the first light all-metal machine, and he became known as the 'Father of the Bicycle'. This again shows how John Penn II cared about his people. He knew Starley well enough to realise that his inventiveness was more in tune with small, light machines than heavy marine steam engines.

The year 1871 also gives a window on another aspect of John Penn II's life: his interest in music. He was known as a competent organist and had a portable organ at The Cedars. He also had a band and there is a record of its appearance at a three-day Grand Fancy Bazaar [501, p74] in aid of the Building Fund for St Peter's Church, Eltham.[23] It is billed as the band of John Penn Esq. and as Mr Penn's Band, along with those of the Royal Artillery, the Metropolitan Police and the 25th Kent regiment. The fact that it was not billed as a works or firm's band could be taken as another indication of how, for him, the firm was inseparable from himself. This band would have played at the fetes held at The Cedars, and other local events.

John Penn II took his two elder sons into partnership in 1872 and the firm became John Penn & Sons. There was a legal partnership agreement, which was sensible, as he was almost certain to leave the partnership before them. It was in the same year that ex-Emperor Napoleon III and his wife

GRAND

FANCY BAZAAR,

IN AID OF THE

BUILDING FUND

OF

St. PETER'S CHURCH,

ELTHAM ROAD, S.E.

JUNE 20th, 21st & 22nd, 1871.

PROGRAMME OF MUSIC

TO BE PERFORMED BY

THE BANDS

OF

THE ROYAL ARTILLERY

JOHN PENN, Esq.,

METROPOLITAN POLICE

AND

25TH KENT LIGHT INFANTRY.

501 Bazaar Band Programme

Eugenie visited The Cedars and admired the fine avenue of elms which John Penn had preserved by the diversion of the road in front the house. The ex-Emperor is reported as saying:

> We never have seen such fine specimens in the whole of France as we see now of this noble tree. There they are hewn down before they come to one-third of their maturity, and consigned to the timber depot for sale.[24]

His visit was occasioned by the Horticultural Exhibition of Fruit and Flowers and he was invited to become President of the Blackheath Horticultural Society. No doubt Mr Penn's band played.

In 1873 both John Penn III and William Penn became members of the Institution of Mechanical Engineers, proposed by their father and Joseph Whitworth. They qualified as being 'over twenty-four years of age and managing an establishment in which engines and other machines are made.' In 1874 John Penn III became a member of the Institution of Civil Engineers.[25]

In 1874 the firm supplied the last large trunk engines to the Royal Navy, for HMS *Neptune*, with 8,000 hp. She later became the *Independencia* of the Brazilian navy. Her 118-inch-diameter cylinders were overtaken by the 123-inch-diameter cylinders for the *Kaiser* and the *Deutschland* for the German navy in the same year. These were the 'swansong' of the large trunk engine, thirty years after the patent. During all this time the Admiralty and foreign navies had been the only buyers of trunk engines and the firm's major buyers of marine steam engines. The majority of cargo vessels were still sailing ships but, with the introduction of the compound, and later, triple-expansion engines this was about to change as their greater efficiency gave steam a competitive advantage over sail.

Several technical developments were bringing about changes in the industry. One was the availability of steel plate for shipbuilding, cheaper in price than wrought iron and, being available in larger plates, cheaper to build with. Steel plate also enabled boilers to be built which could safely operate at higher pressures which, in turn, helped the introduction of compound

502 Trunk engine assembly, Greenwich works

engines. Another was the introduction of new and much better tool steels for use in machining. This might seem minor but was an important development in engineering manufacturing. To take full advantage of the superior performance of the new tool steels it was necessary to have new, more powerful and robust machine tools. These were easily justified investments for the firms which saw their business expanding but very hard to justify based on the cost savings alone. The consequential improvements in the product quality were not foreseen or judged to be significant. The opportunities arising from all these developments were seized by the shipbuilders and marine engineers of the north who were successful in the expanding, low-cost cargo ship business and who, with their modern equipment, came to match Thameside quality at lower cost. The Thameside builders, with their old and cramped facilities, could not respond to these challenges and fewer orders came their way. Penn's did not gain any significant part of the new cargo business and the lignum vitae stern bearing patent had expired by the time of more widespread use of the screw-propeller. The firm did not benefit from the growth in the merchant fleet through either engine orders or royalties.

In addition to this changing situation in the industry it is important to realise that the period 1873 to 1896 is known to economic historians as The Great Depression.[26] Overall economic conditions and the Thameside shipbuilding slump would have increased the firm's difficulty in justifying investment for modernisation. We do not know how this combination of adverse circumstances was seen by the owners. It is likely that they did not, probably could not, recognise it in this simple, hindsight-guided way.

In 1874 John Penn II bought a steam yacht *Pandora*, presumably replacing the *Lara*. She was a Clyde-built, 164-foot, three-masted screw schooner to which he fitted a ninety horsepower compound engine.[27] *Pandora* was a favourite place for him to be. He cruised in her up the Seine and the Rhine and also along the west coast of Italy. She became even more important when he retired from active management of the business in 1875. During these cruises he was able to use his considerable linguistic skills in conversation with the local people, something he would have enjoyed.

In 1874 Thomas Penn had retired from working with the firm.[28] He went to live in Grove Lodge in Lewisham High Street, number 169 opposite the drive to Riverdale House. Rebecca Penn, John Penn I's widow, had lived there for many years; John II had bought it for her.

In 1876 John Penn II took out a patent for an engine which was intended to combine the fuel efficiency of a compound with the power of a simple engine.[29] Normal compound engines had two cylinders of different diameters: a small diameter for the high-pressure expansion and a larger one for the low-pressure. The thrust generated by each cylinder would be about the same. Penn's patent engine had three cylinders of the same diameter. For fuel-efficient cruising one cylinder would act as the high-pressure cylinder and two as the low-pressure cylinder of a compound. For higher speed in combat all three cylinders would act at high pressure, developing twice the power. Such engines were used in five naval ships, three of them for the Royal Navy, all twin-screw vessels using two engines. One was HMS *Northampton* of 1876; she was a second R. Napier, Clyde-built ship engined by Penn. She did not meet performance expectations in trial.[30] In addition there were two ships for the Italian navy, the single-screw *Cristoforo Colombo* and the twin-screw *Italia* with two engines on each shaft [503, p77]. She was a remarkable warship for her times.[31] Like the trunk engine this design was not of interest for merchant vessels. This patent shows that John Penn II's forward thinking was still focused on Admiralty requirements. It seems that he did not foresee

503 *Italia*,
1886

the likely effect the development of the compound engine would have on marine engineering for both merchant and naval ships; neither did his sons.

In 1876 and 1877 John III and William married. Their wives were two daughters of Thomas Lucas who, in 1887, was created first Baronet of Ashstead Park in Surrey. They established themselves in houses at, for John III, 22 Carlton House Terrace, and, for William, 4 Richmond Terrace off Whitehall. They could take the train to the Works in Greenwich and Deptford but, following their father's death, the day-to-day management would have been more in the hands of a professional. It seems likely that their attention to the affairs of the firm was not very intense, certainly less so than their father's at their age. It was certainly not a good management approach for a business facing major strategic challenges.

In 1877 John Penn III became a member of the Council of the Institution of Mechanical Engineers. He served on a subcommittee which found a London property for the Institution to rent when it moved from Birmingham that year and, later on, one to determine what action the Institution should take with regard to new Board of Trade regulations on Inspection of Shipbuilding and Construction of Machinery. Even though he rarely attended meetings of the Council he won the most votes when elected for a second term: a measure of his personal popularity.[32]

The Penn family's oral history which contained the story that John Penn II had a liaison in Paris in the 1820s includes a rumour that near the end of his life he may have been approached for money by the descendants of the affair. There is a little piece of possibly corroborating evidence. In 1877 John Penn asked the office manager, John Coomber, to look in the firm's records to find evidence of the date of his visit to France with the Perkins steam gun and also to look to see if a man called Leplustrier had been employed in any way.[33] The date of Penn's trip to France was concluded to have been between February and May 1828. Leplustier was paid 1s for coach hire on 6 October 1827. There does not seem to be a connection. But – pure speculation – did Leplustrier suggest to Penn that if he ever went to Paris he could stay with an uncle and aunt who kept a clean house in a convenient district. Maybe there was a charming daughter there? Whatever happened then, if it is accepted that he supported that family whilst in need and that he behaved honourably at the time of his marriage, there would be nothing much to hold against him.

When John Penn II retired from the management of the firm he was already in failing health, suffering from paralysis of his limbs and loss of sight. His mind continued to be active and only three days before his death he had returned from a cruise on *Pandora*. He had seen his son William fully

504 John Penn II in his bath chair, mid 1870s

recovered from his earlier riding accident and seemed in good spirits. He suffered a stroke on the evening of Monday 23 September 1878 and never recovered.

His funeral took place on the following Saturday at St Margaret's Church [001 Area Map, p8] in Lee, close to The Cedars.[34] Both the firm's works were closed to enable the men to attend. Fourteen hundred of them marched four abreast, a column a quarter of a mile long, through the streets from Deptford and Greenwich while the shopkeepers on the route closed their doors in respect. The men lined the road between the house and the church and behind them were thousands of people from Blackheath, Deptford, Greenwich and Lee who came to show their respects. The coffin, covered with flowers, gorgeous white lilies and others woven with maidenhair ferns and with wreathes hanging from the sides, was borne from the house to the church by eight men from the works. The music from the church could be heard by the crowds and with Handel's Dead March from *Saul* the coffin was brought out to be interred in the family vault close to the north side of the church. Mrs Pearce, who had cared for John Penn II in his final illness, laid a beautiful bouquet on the coffin at the request of her mistress. The white lilies and other flowers were left on the top of the vault for all to see.

All the family were present at the funeral, men only as was the custom. Sons, sons-in-law, A English (his brother-in-law), Thomas Penn and William Hartree II, both of whom would remember their fathers' funerals – twelve and nineteen years earlier. Amongst the mourners were many notable people from the engineering profession, the Admiralty and foreign navies, managers from the firm, local office holders and neighbours, including Samuel Smiles. The display of grief and respect by his employees and the public was exceptional. The commentaries in the local paper give a good record of what lay behind this.

First, about him as an employer:

> No man ever more justly appreciated the duties and obligations of that relation more efficiently and conscientiously discharged them than Mr. Penn. Always maintaining his authority and dignity, and paying proper heed to his own interests in his dealings with those in his employment, yet he conscientiously recognised what was due to them, and was kindly considerate of their interests and welfare.

> How well Mr. Penn acted his part as an employer will be gratefully acknowledged by those who have worked for him for the longest period, and we may mention as an illustration of the kindly interest he felt in their welfare that to the last he could remember the names of his oldest hands and applications for assistance from them always received his sympathising attention; and the affectionate regard in which he is held by the men in the employment of the firm will be manifest today as hundreds of them will gather in silent sorrow to witness the obsequies of their old and honoured master...

> A great employer of labour, he has illustrated how practicable it is to maintain between the employer and the employed the most cordial relations – always properly insisting on his rights in his position, he has ever recognised his duties. He did not regard his men as mere engines of production, from whose labour it was desirable to extract the largest amount of profit, without regard to their circumstances and welfare.[35]

John Bourne, a personal friend for 40 years, wrote in *The Engineer*:

> Mr. Penn's reputation was gradually built up by a series of successes: it owned no part of its splendour to accidental or adventitious circumstances, and while unique, it will therefore be also enduring. In whatever Mr. Penn did he excelled. As a workman he had no equal in his own or any other factory, in every department, whether in the smithy or the turning shop, or the fitting shop, or any other he could take the tools out of the men's hands and show them how the work should be performed. This capability gave him great power over the workmen, and enabled him to model his factory so that it became a pattern to all others in the kingdom. He paid his men liberally, but he would have no drones, and he established such improved modes of working that high quality became reconciled with economical production. He quickened the speed of all his tools so as to enable them to turn out more work in a given time, and he was one of the first to avail himself of the aids to accuracy afforded by the face-plates and gauges, and other instruments of precision, constructed by Sir Joseph Whitworth. From the beginning of his career Mr. Penn's constant aim was the realisation of the highest degree of excellence, and he certainly more than any of his contemporaries succeeded in realising that aspiration.[36]

All this is entirely consistent with the picture presented about the importance of the skills of the workforce to the achievement of his business success.

Second, about him in social life.

> Nothing could be more beautiful than his tender devotion to his wife, who in the unseen

works of charity in which he was engaged was his kindly almoner and assistant, and his love for his children not only continued without abatement, but intensified as he grew older, and found a new and interesting development in his affection for grandchildren. We have remarked on the liberality of Mr. Penn in aiding workmen in difficulty or distress, but his philanthropy was not confined to them, his general benevolence and kindness were well known. No case of true distress that came to Mr. Penn was ever disregarded, but if his charity was generous it was also discriminating. It was his highest pleasure to relieve honest poverty and to mitigate, by timely liberality the distress of the afflicted and bereaved...

...a devoted father; instead of his interest in his children and his loving sympathy with them diminishing as he grew older, it increased. Nothing gave him such pleasure as to gather them around him in the paternal home.[37]

Sadly, like his father, he would have known his grandchildren only in their infancy.

Another picture of John Penn II as a parent comes from letters written from school by William to his mother and to his brother John III.[38] They show that he was rather frightened of his father and felt inhibited in what he could ask or tell him; this seems very understandable in the social context of the times.

Another comment is interesting in view of John Penn I's political venture, of which there is no mention.

Although he took no conspicuous part in politics, and was equally esteemed by men of both parties, yet Mr. Penn was by conviction firmly and intelligently devoted to the Conservative cause, and if he had ever desired Parliamentary honours he would have doubtless obtained a seat as the representative of his native borough, which was so justly proud of him.[39]

Other comments:

A man of culture and refined taste, his residence was a fitting abode for a merchant prince...[40]

Mr. Penn was endowed by nature with rare social qualities, and was of a most hospitable disposition.[41]

On his work there are the words:

Superiority is in every respect his chief aim.

Often quoted are his words:

I cannot afford to turn out second rate work. I must have the best workmen and the best materials.

He put all these personal qualities into effect and, in prosperous times, built his business success on them. Quality enabled him to attract premium priced business which, in turn, produced the profits which supported his lifestyle and enabled him to pay his men well.

The threats to the firm inherent in this strategy had begun to emerge at the time of his death. His workforce of best workmen was ageing. The firm's equipment was becoming increasingly obsolete. The high-cost locations and layouts of the works were becoming an increasing competitive disadvantage as the industry changed and the Thameside yards' share of the national shipbuilding market declined. The more modern, better-located factories built for lower-cost engines were becoming able to compete in the quality market. A vision of this kind is easy to see with hindsight. It is difficult for an entrepreneur to see his future in such terms although, as we have seen, there were warnings.

A touching recognition of John Penn II, engineer, came in the form of an Institution of Mechanical Engineers commemorative plate for a conference in 1879. It depicted George Stephenson and *Rocket* and was inscribed 'George Stephenson First President 1847–1848' and, lettered round the edge, the names 'Trevithick, Fairbairn, Parsons, Watt, Whitworth, Maudslay, Penn'. Here, he was placed amongst the highest ranks of mechanical engineers.[42]

His will was written in 1875 with four subsequent codicils. The partnership agreement is referred to and under it the two remaining partners, John Penn III and William, had to pay £80,000 to the estate as John Penn II's share of the business. Ellen received £300,000 plus a life interest in The Cedars and its contents, and also shares in the Grand Junction, West Middlesex, Southwark, and Vauxhall and East London Water Companies (similar to John Penn I's Gas Works shares to his wife). John Penn III received £40,000, William £25,000, Frank and Alfred £15,000 each, increased by £25,000 by codicil. His three Trustees received £3,000 each and his cousin Thomas Penn the house, Grove Lodge where he lived in Lewisham. The residue was to be shared from six equal parts, one to each of the four sons and one to each of the two daughters, who would receive one third absolutely and two thirds in trust. The Probate valuation was 'less than £1,000,000'.

There were no bequests to charities, nor any to named individuals such as personal servants. He probably expected Ellen would look after charities. The absence of personal bequests, to Mrs Pearce, who had cared for him and who placed Ellen's flowers on the coffin at he funeral, or Mr Sweny his private secretary or Captain Hurst of *Pandora* for example, is suprising but may be understandable when it is remembered that he looked upon all his employees as, in a sense, personal servants and may not have wished to differentiate amongst them.

Note on Steam Boilers and Compound Engines

The development of the steam engine to use higher pressure, 150 to 200 psi, was made in many steps and took some thirty years. In the early years there was still a lot of argument about the validity of the claim that higher pressure would lead to greater efficiency. The theory of thermodynamics had not been developed to the point where the claim could be theoretically proved, and even when it was many engineers did not understand it.

Overcoming the practical difficulties in terms of boiler and engine materials, design and manufacture was inevitably a gradual process. The availability of steels from the Bessemer and Gilchrist-Thomas processes in the 1870s was a very significant contribution. These steels could be made stronger than wrought iron, in larger-sized components and cheaper. The development of techniques for the manufacture of tubes in steel and in brass which could withstand higher pressures was another important contribution. Brass tubing was important for the development of condensers. Other relevant developments were in the piston rings and piston rod and valve seals, the development of mineral oil-based lubricants which could be used at higher temperatures, and subsequently the introduction of centralised forced lubrication systems. Previously lubrication relied on regular manual refilling of oil and grease boxes, many of which were in very inaccessible, dark places; hence sometimes forgotten – resulting in overheated bearings.

The idea of the compound engine was to make full use of the pressure of the steam. In the simple engine the pressure of the steam in the cylinder at the end on the stroke was lost as the steam went to the condenser. In a compound engine the steam was introduced into a second cylinder and applied its remaining pressure to another larger piston and then passed to the condenser. That was double expansion, ordinary compound. Once its engineering problems were overcome the triple-expansion engine followed, using even higher boiler pressures and achieving greater efficiency. This engine enabled steam to compete very effectively with sail in the cargo trade and was widely used in naval ships. The quadruple-expansion engine followed, but its use was restricted to rather special applications.

Most compound engines were of a guided crosshead design with the cylinders mounted vertically. In paddle ships they were mounted below the paddle shaft, whereas in screw ships they were mounted above the propeller shaft and known as inverted vertical engines.

6. The Next Generation (1878–1899)

The obituaries and appreciations of John Penn II are impressive and, even if slightly discounted as eulogies written in the language of their time, they remain so. The story has been told about his father, who gave him a fine training, early opportunities and left to him a business in good shape. The story has been unable to tell anything about his mother, who gave him half his genes and his early upbringing; she should also be remembered when reading his praises.

In today's more mundane terms it could be said 'he'll be a hard act to follow', but he had to be followed. The firm had orders to complete and new ones to gain, it had bills to collect and bills to pay. The staff was in place; his two elder sons John III and William had been managing the business for the last three years and had been partners for six. John had gained engineering knowledge in the firm and had become an Associate of the Institution of Civil Engineers in 1874 and became a full Member in 1880. He was a proponent of compound engines and particularly of the firm's three-cylinder patent of which, as mentioned in the previous chapter, five were supplied to the British and Italian navies from the mid-1870s into the 1880s (Appendix 2, Table 2).

The design of the fighting ship was in a state of continuous change from the 1860s onwards. Several different lines of development were occurring simultaneously. The move from broadside-mounted guns to guns mounted on deck in rotating armoured turrets; the development of explosive and armour-piercing shells which led to competition between the penetrative power of the artillery against the protective strength of the armour plate: the development of special steels became a crucial part of this. Also there was the change from smooth to rifled bore gun barrels and from muzzle to breech loading, which together increased the accuracy and rapidity of fire. The effect of all these changes, thicker armour, bigger guns and heavier shells, was to increase the weight of the ship and led to the demand for still more powerful engines to achieve high speeds. The increased power had to be achieved with the least increase in engine and boiler weight and at improved coal consumption as bunkers full of coal were yet more weight. The marine engineering development which first met this challenge through the 1870s and 1880s was the compound engine working at pressures of 60 to120 psi. Defensive armour also reduced the need to keep the engines low in the hull and allowed engines with vertical cylinders, guided crossheads and connecting rods, as used in merchant ships, to be used by the Navy, thus eliminating the usefulness of the main design feature of the Penn's trunk engine. These developments rendered ships such as HMS *Warrior* and *Devastation* obsolete. They and their sister ships had, without firing a shot in battle, but acting as the 'ultimate deterrents' of their day, ensured the supremacy of the Royal Navy.

In addition to this a variety of other developments were taking place. In the early days steam on board ship was used only as a source of power for propulsion; everything else was done by man-power. It was not until the 1860s that donkey engines to provide power for on-deck winches and windlasses came into general use. As ships became heavier, steering by men at the wheel became less and less effective. It was in the late 1860s that a useful power-steering mechanism became available. John Macfarlane Gray's device was first used in *Great Eastern* and then by the Navy in HMS *Northumberland* and *Monarch*. *Warrior* had not been fitted with power steering. Once the overall design principles were established, power-steering gear became available from many marine engineers and its use became widespread in the 1870s. The coming of electricity to ships was another important development of the 1880s. It first came to provide lighting on passenger vessels and, at the same time, was used to illuminate working areas such as the engine and boiler rooms and passageways. The advantages of well-lit and hence more efficiently operated machinery were obvious to the Navy also. (If you visit *Warrior* think of working down in those places by the light of a few dim oil lamps, trying to put oil or grease in the right place and so on, or if fetching coal from the bunkers, working by the light of a candle on your hat brim like an old-fashioned coal miner – and doing all this at temperatures of 35° to 40° C.)

A consequence of all these developments was to turn the operation of the ship into a task needing more and more technical knowledge. Developments in naval gunnery were also becoming increasingly technical and with the arrival of the torpedo in 1870 came yet another technology to be mastered. A Naval College of Engineering was founded in 1879 at Keyham and there was also a Gunnery School, but the Royal Navy's attitude to the Engineer Officer, and other technical officers such as Gunnery, remained unchanged. Committees reviewed the situation but their recommendations to improve the status of engineer and technical officers were fought off by the senior serving and retired executive officers who had political influence. Concern was expressed from outside naval circles. In 1877 Mr E. J. Reed, a past Chief Constructor to the Navy, in a letter to *The Times*, wrote that the naval engineer officer felt himself to be

> ...a snubbed, subordinated man, with dozens of officers put above him to look down upon him, and keep him in the inferior place which the Admiralty had assigned to him.

and continued

> If this Navy of which I am writing belonged to the few politicians and Admirals who regulate it we might smile at the absurdity of such arrangements, and there leave the matter. But...the Navy belongs to the people of Britain, and the depression, I would even say the degradation of a class of officers upon whom its efficiency and glory must so largely depend in the future, is a matter of the most serious public concern...It is shameful to leave an evil of this kind for redress until the engineers themselves require and demand it. Their interest in the matter, however great, is only secondary; it is for the country's interest that the position of naval engineers should be raised to a level corresponding to the greatness of their present trust, and to the weight of their enlarged responsibilities.[1]

Over a decade later there was still a need for engineer officer recruits.[2] The required number did not come forward and the retirement age was raised to overcome the shortage. Keyham was not attracting sufficient entrants of the required standard of education. When the headmasters of the Public Schools, where the born-to-lead would be found, were asked why this was so they said it was due to the poor prospects the Navy offered to engineers. The situation of the Navy's engineers remained unsatisfactory. Social conservatism continued to hamper the efficiency of the service.

In 1880 a multi-volume work entitled *Great Industries of Great Britain* appeared. It contained a series of articles entitled *Model Establishments*. The first of these, written by Robert Smiles (no relation to Samuel), was *Messrs. John Penn and Sons, Marine Engineers, Greenwich*.[3]

It is in this account of the firm's history that John Penn I's political venture and possible friendship with William Cobbett is mentioned. It must have been told to Smiles by John III or William (possibly Cobbett was confused with Cubitt).

In the first paragraph Smiles points out that the works layout is not suitable to be considered for what is required of a *Model Establishment*. After the historical section he goes on to describe the office and the rooms for meetings with customers, which contained models of engines built by the firm. These were usually built by the firm's apprentices and were on display to show prospective customers. Some of these models of Penn oscillating, trunk and patent compound engines can be seen in the Marine Engineering gallery of the Science Museum, along with those by competitors. He mentions the Counting House, which kept the records which were the source of the information on the Steam Gun which was quoted earlier. He also describes the Drawing Office, admirably lit, in which

> ...the complete drawings and specifications are prepared by chiefs of departments, in concert with the heads of the firm. From the finished designs working drawings are made, showing in exact proportions the minutest details, down to rivet and bolt holes. These drawings are passed to the head foremen in the different shops, who are responsible for the production of the numerous and varied parts that are brought into harmonious combination in a vast and complex machine.

This coincides with the earlier visitors' reports and importantly adds the role of designers. The degree of detail on the drawings shows the firm to be advanced for its time. The report also shows that Smiles was a journalist more than an engineer.

Smiles goes on to make the point that there is a steep slope from the entrance at the junction of Lewisham Road and John Penn Street to the offices and then again from the offices to the Erecting Shop. He provides a sketch map of the Greenwich site which, together with old Ordnance Survey maps, provides the basis for the Works Layout. [420, p68]

Interestingly, he makes a strong point about the importance of the Pattern Shop where the patterns for all castings were made. This is very valid as pattern-making is the first stage in the making of castings, and errors in it are hard to rectify. It is a specialist, skilled woodworker's job. Smiles goes on to say how a catalogue of these patterns could make 'a valuable contribution to the history of steam navigation'. He describes the Smiths' Shop with its sixty hearths; the Foundry in which both iron and brass and bronze castings are made, with its five Penn-made cranes which cover the whole area; and the Small Turnery with its excellent machine tools where smaller engines are made. He refers to one for 'the somewhat unpopular craft known as steam launches'. He then describes the Erecting Shop and Heavy Turnery of four bays and a lean-to. Apparently this structure had been erected over the site of a previous smaller shop which was not unroofed before the new one was complete. There is no mention of when this happened but it is typical of unplanned, piecemeal expansion. There were two lines of tramways running across the bays and as many as twenty overhead cranes running along them. Here he saw some of the firm's remarkable machine tools of its own design. The one for crankshafts described by the Engineers' Society was still evident, as also were the huge lathe and planing machine. He mentions a new tool for boring and drilling the tube-plates for surface condensers. He gives a brief description of the Deptford Boiler Works and mentions some specialist machines there. He talked to some employees and found them all full of praise for the firm. One specially mentioned 'the number of widows that Mrs. John Penn, of The Cedars – a true "Lady Bountiful" – had upon her books'.

This does not add much to the reports of the earlier visits but it leaves the impression that there had not been much investment in new machinery as none is mentioned. Were the firm's enormous old machine tools becoming obsolete? Did the firm invest in new machine tools better suited to the new products such as smaller-diameter cylinders and composite steel crankshafts? Sadly there are no records which would provide an answer.

None of the reports on visits to the works tell anything about the commercial aspects of the business. There is nothing about what today we call the marketing of the firm or about the selling of its products. Who represented the firm to the customers? From Appendix 2 and the underlying data it seems clear that the firm's main customers were the Admiralty and Thameside shipyards building river and coastal steamers for local and foreign use. It would have been fairly easy to keep in personal contact with them. The Penn oscillating engine of the Weymouth pleasure steamer *Empress*, built by Samuda in 1879, now in the Southampton Maritime Museum, is a reminder of these sales. It is not known how the firm tried to sell to other British yards, or even if it tried at all. It is noticeable that in the weekly issues of the journal *Engineering* for 1888, a time of deep depression, there were no advertisements for John Penn & Sons whilst Thorneycroft and Yarrow advertised every week.

601 1879 Oscillating Engine from *Empress*

All the Penn sons were keen sportsmen. They would have learnt to play cricket at school and three of them played for Kent. Frank was a good batsman and played over a hundred innings between 1875 and 1881. He also played for England against Australia in 1880. William, who had played in the 1867 Eton–Harrow match, played for Kent thirty-one times between 1871 and 1878. Alfred was a bowler and played sixty-three times between 1875 and 1874. Frank junior also played a few times in the early 1900s.[4] Golf was another important activity. The three elder sons joined Royal Blackheath Golf Club in 1877. William won a competition 1881, Frank in 1877 and 1878 and John III won thirteen between 1880 and 1885. In 1882 they all joined London Scottish, which later became Royal Wimbledon. John III became Captain of Royal Blackheath from 1881 to 1883. He was also a founding member of Royal St George's, Sandwich.[5] Alfred had a racing yacht. They all enjoyed game shooting. William's Game Book of 1875 details shooting parties with all the brothers, the prospective brothers-in-law and a maternal cousin taking part. Leases of shoots were taken

602 John Penn III, 'dressed for a shoot'

for weeks at a time. All these activities as gentlemen of leisure would have diverted their attention from the management of the firm and increasingly left it to a professional manager. Were they, the owners, aware of the strategic threat the business was facing? Did they feel that there was little they could do about it, so why worry? Did they feel their lifestyles were at stake? Sadly, these are unanswerable questions.

It happened that at the time of the 1881 Census most of the family were at The Cedars, which adds to the picture of them. Present were Ellen; John III with his wife Amy and two daughters aged three and one; William with his wife Constance (a sister of Amy), a son and a daughter aged three and one; Alfred; Ellen with her husband and daughter aged one; and Isabella and her husband with baby son; a total of sixteen members of the family spanning three generations. With them were twenty-one servants: a butler, a valet, a cook, four ladies' maids, four housemaids, two nursemaids and five nurse domestics, a parlour maid, a kitchen maid and a scullery maid. This gives a good picture of the lifestyle they enjoyed; for a family of that size and social standing it was not too remarkable at the time. It confirms that they were all at least maintaining their lifestyles and possibly improving on their social positions. Daughter Ellen's husband was Joseph Fletcher Green of the family which ran a shipbuilding and repair yard at Blackwall on the Middlesex bank of Bow Creek and to which the firm had supplied many engines. Isabella's husband, Frederick Stokes, was a solicitor and another sportsman; he played cricket for Kent and captained England in the first England vs Scotland rugby international. Included in the census return was a note that Penn's firm employed nine hundred and seventy men and boys. Later two houses, West Lodge and The Cottage, were built for the two daughters and their families on the eastern boundary of The Cedars estate north of the railway line, in Love Lane – now called Heath Lane.

The rebuilding of Deptford Bridge in 1883[6] would have given a small improvement to the firm's operations. The bracing of the bridge to support heavy loads, which was well remembered by employees, would have been required less frequently. These heavy load movements took place at night or in the early hours to minimise disruption of traffic. Horses with muffled shoes were used at night. Traction engines could be used by day.

In 1884 the Penn Almshouses in South Street, Greenwich were completed and officially opened early the following year.[7] John Penn II had been a trustee of the Jubilee Almshouses. After his death his widow, Ellen, created a new foundation in his memory which built a block of eight almshouses complete with a chapel (Plate Ib). The design, construction and finishing were all done to standards consistent with those John Penn applied to his engines. All was of the best from

603 Penn Almshouses, South Street, Greenwich

especially strong foundations, due to the vibrations from the neighbouring railway which is no longer there, to the brick and Portland stone exterior and to the interior flooring and finishing. Ellen was determined that the building would in be all ways a fitting memorial to John Penn II. The main purpose was to provide for poor men and their widows over sixty years of age who had worked at the firm's factories. She endowed the charity to provide a small income to the residents and a living-in matron.

The chapel suffered damage in World War II. During the war the Mary Ann Smith almshouse charity of Greenwich had its buildings completely destroyed. In 1955 the two came together under a joint family trust. The chapel at the Penn Almshouses was rebuilt to create two more houses so there would be room for ten residents The Almshouses now form part of the housing provision of the local authority, which pays the residents' rents, but the upkeep and modernisation of the buildings continues to be the responsibility of the Penn and Smith families' trust. The original endowments are exhausted and funds are needed. The almshouses, which have been providing housing for more than one hundred and twenty years, are the most enduring, visible memorial to John Penn and the firm (see Appendix 4).

Thomas Penn died in 1886 aged 69, at his home in Grove House, Lewisham. In 1889 Alfred, John and Ellen Penn's youngest son, died at the age of 34. Both were buried in the family vault.

The 1880s were difficult times. The figures in Appendix 2, Table 1 show this as the decade in which the firm made the least engines in fifty years, with only forty-four recorded. A report in *The Times* of 25 January 1888 tells of 'Distress in Greenwich and Deptford'. A large number of people were dependent on philanthropy. 'The works of John Penn and Sons have just been re-opened,

604 John Penn III

after being at almost a standstill for a considerable period.' There were other prospects for local employment on the Blackwall Tunnel and also the London, Dover and Chatham railway extension.

In 1889 the firm was incorporated as a private limited company named John Penn and Sons Limited, and the business was sold by the partnership to the new company.[8] The Memorandum and Articles give the company's share value as £150,000, made up of fifteen hundred shares of £100 each. John III and William were the two principal shareholders. They were both directors, John being named as Chairman, and had rights to three, and later four, votes each at Board Meetings plus the requirement that one must be present at any Board Meeting. There were two other directors: H. H. Fowler MP, and John Percy Hall, the Managing Director. The other shareholders were Joseph and Ellen Green (née Penn), one share each; Ellen Penn (widow of John II), one share; Frank (son of John II) and Grace Penn, one share each; Frederic and Isabella Stokes (née Penn), he a solicitor, one share each. All the shares were retained in the family. John Percy Hall was the professional manager who ran the company day to day.

The sale was agreed on 1 January 1889, the agreement signed on 6 August and completed on 1 October. It included the engine factory, iron foundry, workshops, etc. in the parish of St Alphage, Greenwich; properties 98 to 110, Blackheath Road, Greenwich, one of which was a reading room for the employees; the boiler factory and premises known as Deptford Pier in the parish of St Nicholas, Deptford; messuage, stables, land and premises in Slaughter House Lane in the parish of St Nicholas, Deptford; all the machinery and furniture including a floating workshop and barges; all the work in progress in the factories, the orders received and the financial assets and liabilities. The properties were largely freehold but some were leasehold and the leases were sold to the company. John III and William were running the business in the name of the company from 6 August. Of the amount paid under the agreement, £156,550:0s:8d was treated as the consideration for the freehold and leasehold premises and the chattels and other property; that is the fixed assets. The partners put that consideration into the company in return for their shares. The books of account and other documents of the partnership remained the property of the partners; their subsequent loss cannot be held against the company.

There are two likely reasons for the change in company structure. One is that in a partnership the partners can be individually liable in the case of the business's bankruptcy. If this seems at all likely it would be sensible to separate the legal responsibilities of the business and of the owners. The formation of a company largely achieves this. The other is that the establishment of a company simplifies the procedures if others wish to become shareholders or to acquire the business in order to integrate it into their own operations. Shipbuilding suffered a fallback in orders in the 1870s and 1880s, with the Thames suffering more than other locations, and the brothers may well have been concerned for the future of their business. The partners may have come to realise that the firm's location and layout were far from ideal, its cost structure uncompetitive and the need for investment large. Bearing in mind the business conditions at the time, the formation of a company was a sensible thing to do.

After the defeat of France in the Franco-Prussian War the traditional threat to Britain from France had diminished. The growing threat now came from the new united Germany. It was not quickly noticed, but once it had been a new naval building programme was initiated. This culminated in the Naval Defence Act of 1889. Following this Act orders from the Navy once again became an important part of the output of private yards and the firm benefited with orders for engines. This increase in naval requirement coincided with the successful development of the triple-expansion engine with its higher-pressure boilers which had taken place largely in the merchant fleet in the 1880s. In most years of the 1890s[9] the firm provided triple-expansion compound engines to the Navy, from HMS *Sappho (2)* operating at 150 psi in 1891 to HMS *Goliath* using 300 psi in 1898. The engine for HMS *Magnificent* (1894) shows that these engines, designed under the management of John Percy Hall and using all the latest developments in materials technology, retained all the Penn characteristics of minimisation of weight and simplicity of design.[10] The firm preferred fire-tube to water-tube boilers and a forced draught to a pressurised stokehold in order to increase the boilers' rating. The records show engines for only sixty-six home waters merchant vessels between 1870 and 1899 (Appendix 2, Table 3). Oscillating and compound engines were in roughly equal numbers. There is no record of the firm supplying triple-expansion engines for merchant vessels.

605 Penn triple expansion engine for HMS *Magnificent*, 1894

The next major development in marine engineering, the steam turbine, started its development in the 1880s. In a turbine the shaft is rotated by high-pressure steam rushing onto shaped blades on the circumference of the rotor. In Britain the pioneer of the turbine was Charles Parsons, whose first turbines were used to drive electricity generators. The uninvited appearance of his turbine-powered yacht *Turbinia* running at high speed through the fleet at the 1897 Spithead review attracted a great deal of attention. Following this the Admiralty ordered the first turbine-powered warship. It was clear that the turbine gave far more power for the same weight of engine than a triple-expansion compound. The early turbine-powered vessels were small and fast and there were many problems to overcome before the turbine could be used for large ships. The rotational speed of a turbine is much higher than needed for ships' propellers so it was necessary to use gearing between the turbine and the propeller shaft. Gear design and manufacturing needed extensive development. The mathematical principles of gear design were by then well understood; a big change since John Penn I's day. This, combined with the recent developments in gear steels, in machine tools and accuracy of machining made it possible to manufacture reliable, high-power turbine drive systems. By the early 1900s, these were being used for large liners and warships.

606 HMS *Magnificent*, 1894

Again, in 1891, a census year, there is some information about the family. Ellen was away from home but there was a housekeeper and six servants in the house with a gatekeeper at the Lodge and a gardener in the Cottage at The Cedars. John Penn III and family were also away from home at 22 Carlton House Terrace but a butler, a housekeeper, two housemaids, kitchen maid, scullery maid, two footmen and a coachman were in residence, again giving some idea of the style of life. The house has been replaced by a modern building but most of the terrace remains. William Penn, wife Constance and eldest son Eric Frank, two daughters and twin sons lived at 4 Richmond Terrace, Whitehall, now government offices. For the census William was the only family member at home. In the return his occupation is given as 'Engine Builder'. The domestic complement was a butler, two footmen and three maids. The ladies' maids would have been away with their mistresses. These two London addresses were very desirable places to live. Ellen continued to make The Cedars and its grounds available for charitable events. Five thousand people attended a temperance fete in aid of the Seaman's Hospital in 1889.

John Penn III was a very sociable man and joined several clubs.[11] There he could have met Members of Parliament and other politically minded people and developed an interest in political matters. He may have remembered hearing about his grandfather's venture in the 1832 general election. In 1891 the then Lord Lewisham and fifth Earl of Dartmouth, a descendant of John Penn I's early customer, died. His son Viscount Lewisham, who had been the Conservative MP for West Kent and then Lewisham since 1878, was elevated to the peerage and to the House of Lords. This caused a by-election in the Lewisham constituency and in August, John Penn III stood as the candidate for the Conservative party. He was opposed by Mr G .S. Warmington, then the mayor of Lewisham.

The Times reported the meetings held by the candidates and those held on their behalf. They were lively events. Polling was on 26 August and it is reported as an orderly day.[12] A story of note was the presence of a fine St Bernard dog walking in the streets wearing a coat bearing the message

'Vote for Mr. Penn, and don't forget it.' This dog, Prince, supporting the Conservative candidate was a familiar sight at elections in South London. John Penn III won with a majority of 1,693. This election would have pleased his grandfather. His grandson had won and many of the changes he had spoken for sixty years earlier had been fulfilled. The Reform Acts of 1867, 1884 and 1885 had created a broad household, male, franchise. In 1868 the tythes or church rate had been abolished and since 1872 election had been by secret ballot.

John Penn III entered the House of Commons in 1892. His maiden speech was in March when he explained to the House the difficulty in trying to make comparisons between naval and merchant vessel performances.[13] He did not make the point that was strongly being made in the profession that the difference in quality and status of the engineer officers could be a factor.[14] He also supported the setting up of an Interim Committee on the question of the type of boiler and draught system to be used in naval vessels. In 1892 there was a General Election and he was returned for Lewisham with an increased majority of 2,414. He was returned unopposed in the General Elections of 1895 and 1900, an achievement which, according to the *Lewisham Gazette*, 'was due as much to his popularity amongst his political opponents as to his undoubted strength in the constituency'.

In every year bar 1893 he asked questions in the House about the engineering complements in naval ships and about the number of entrants to the Naval Engineering College at Keyham.[15] He knew the weaknesses in the Navy's engineering complement and wanted to be sure they were not forgotten. He limited his questions to the uncontroversial subject of numbers, which was proper questioning of the Navy's effectiveness in implementation of its own policy. He avoided the contentious issues concerning engineer officers' rank and status in the Navy which would require a change of policy; the difficulties of which he would have been well aware. This issue was known in parliament as the 'Engineer Battle'. He also regularly asked questions concerning the trials of the Belleville water-tube boiler. This matter was politically tricky in a different way because Belleville was a French company with which there would need to be a licence agreement and the old anti-French prejudices coloured the argument. Penn was wary of water-tube boilers because, although more efficient, they were more difficult to make and to maintain. The subject was so contentious that the Interim Committee continued its deliberations until beyond his time in parliament. This was the 'Boiler Battle'.

These two 'Battles' were the most discussed naval issues in Parliament in the 1890s. John Penn III seems to have quietly and persistently let his views be known, both in and out of the House, and avoided controversy. One constituency-related question concerned the need for the returning wounded from the South African War to have to go through customs clearance. He also spoke on the Great Eastern Railway Company's pension bill, clarifying some points from his knowledge as a director of the Company. During his time in parliament MPs received no salary or expenses. Most were gentlemen of means.

Golf played a large part in John Penn III's parliamentary career. In those days the annual parliamentary competitions were reported stage by stage in the sports columns of *The Times*. According to his obituary in *The Times* John Penn III was 'a leading parliamentary golfer'.[16] His Blackheath playing seemed to take a back seat. He enjoyed arranging private matches, particularly foursomes, in which Mr Balfour, Leader of the House and later the Prime Minister, often took part. During the autumn parliamentary recesses John Penn III rented Archerfield, a fine house at Dirlton in

East Lothian – between Gullane and North Berwick. There was a private course in the grounds to which he had improvements made and where matches were played amongst his house guests. Political friends and family members came for the shooting and the golf, which was also played on neighbouring courses. This was on Mr Balfour's home ground so he and his brother were frequent visitors. Archerfield has been recently renovated and has two golf courses in its grounds. The *Times* obituary specially mentions a thirty-six-hole singles match between Penn and Balfour at the Honour Oak and Forest Hills course in South London which went to the last hole, when Balfour won.

John Penn III was conscientious about his contributions in the House on subjects which he knew well, and about his constituents' concerns. He seems to have looked upon the House more as a gentlemen's club than as a place from which he could take up high-profile causes. His view of politics was not strongly partisan. At one time he was invited to contribute a lecture to a series being given at the Lewisham Liberal Club.[17] He told them that the invitation was one of the most courteous acts ever shown towards him, he had been glad to be with them and that he hoped it would not be the last time he was invited as he would happily come again. There were some raised eyebrows amongst his local Conservative colleagues, which he quickly pointed out were totally misplaced.

During the 1890s John III was Chairman of John Penn and Sons Limited, a director of the Great Eastern Railway Company, a director of the Kent Waterworks and had been Treasurer of the Miller Hospital and Royal Kent Dispensary at Greenwich from 1878, as well as being MP for Lewisham.[18] In 1900, due to his local standing, there was a move towards asking him to become mayor of the new borough of Lewisham.[19] It seems he made it clear that he did not wish to add that role to his other duties. He presented the new borough with a mace. The Miller Hospital was a very important local charity. During John III's time as Treasurer the Presidency was held by two Earls of Dartmouth. There is no record of his brothers undertaking such public roles.

An unusual contract for the company was the supply of the machinery for two water-jet-propelled lifeboats in 1894. The jets were arranged to give thrust both forward and astern and port and starboard. One of these was the *City of Glasgow*, which served at Harwich; the other went to Holland. There is a model of *City of Glasgow* in the Science Museum. It is worth noting that oscillating engines were still being built in the 1880s and 90s. Some of the Thames steamers of 1898 had engines of the same size as those which had been made in 1837. The Penn oscillating engine had a product life of nearly sixty years, which shows that there continued to be applications where the simple, old designs held the advantage. In this context it is interesting to note Rear-Admiral Judd, who had joined Woolwich Arsenal in 1866, saying at a 1922 meeting of The Newcomen Society:

> Penn's oscillating engine had always been his favourite, and he always admired Penn's works at Greenwich.[20]

During the life of Penn's oscillating engine design the basics remained constant. The most obvious changes were in the positioning and drive arrangements of the air pump or pumps in order to minimise the space required for the engine [202, 208, 410 and 601 on pages 26, 32, 59 and 85].

Although John Penn II's stern bearing patent had expired long ago, it is interesting to note that lignum vitae bearings were used in the external bracket propeller shaft supports in the battleship HMS *Prince George*. They are also referred to in the 1907 edition of *A Text-Book of Mechanical Engineering*, using the SS *Iberia* as an example. Wood propeller shaft stern bearings continued to be used in naval and merchant vessels even after reliable gland seals had been developed in the 1950s and 60s.

In 1895 William Hartree II moved to Tunbridge Wells. He had been an Associate of the Institution of Civil Engineers since 1867 and an Associate Member since 1879; he never became a Member. Due to his inheritance from John Penn I as a son of Charlotte Penn he did not need to work at a well-paid job. It is likely that he retired from the firm before, or at, this time. The Company records show that during the 1890s William Penn moved from Richmond Terrace to The Cedars and then to Taverham Hall just north of Norwich. It was fine country house for hosting shooting parties; it is now a school.

The years 1897 and 1898 were those of a major industrial issue known as the 'Engineers' Dispute'.[21] At issue was the length of the working day. The Union wanted a reduction from nine to eight hours. The Employers fought this because it would increase the amount of overtime and so raise costs. It became a nationwide stand-off between the Federation of Engineering Employers and the Amalgamated Engineering Union. There were strikes by union members and lock-outs of unionised workers. John Penn and Sons was a Federation member, was subject to a union strike and locked out the union members. The local focus was Humphreys, Tennant & Dyke's works in Deptford where some unionised workers staged a 'sit-in'. A consequence was that the number of people on relief in Deptford rose to over four hundred while Greenwich had one hundred and twenty.[22] In giving witness to a House of Commons select committee, John Penn III stated that the firm did not differentiate between union members and non-members, that he did not know whether it paid union rate, but he did know that it was never short of men with the right ability. He was of the opinion that wage rates depended on the prices which could be obtained for the contracts undertaken.[23]

There was an increase in naval orders in the 1890s (Appendix 2, Table 3), although most of these were for small pinnaces and launches. It is most unlikely that the firm would have been cost competitive against the shipbuilders in the North, where most commercial vessels were being built. It seems that the orders coming in were not enough to keep the company solvent. In 1899 private negotiations took place for the sale of the business to Thames Ironworks and Shipbuilding Limited, which was completed that summer.[24] The legal winding-up of the company took some time with an Extraordinary General Meeting in April 1900 and the final return on May 1901. Frederick Stokes, one of John Penn II's sons-in-law, acted as liquidator. After more than one hundred years the name of John Penn was no longer in current business use in the engineering world of Greenwich, the Thames or anywhere in the world.

It seems sad now and was sad for those involved. Although it was the end of John Penn and Sons it was not the end of engineering manufacturing work being carried out at the Greenwich and Deptford sites and many of the employees kept their jobs. The continuation of the works' story is the subject of the next chapter. John Penn III ended his association with the business. William Penn became a director of the new company Thames Ironworks, Shipbuilding and Engineering Ltd.

The 'Engineer Battle' over the status of engineer officers in the Navy came alive again in 1902 when Sir John Fisher, the First Sea Lord, stated his policy as 'One System of Supply. One System of Entry. One System of Training' for all officers of the executive/military and engineer branches of the Navy.[25] This was grudgingly accepted by the diehards when applied to new recruits, but they could not agree to it being applied to existing engineer officers. A committee tried to put forward recommendations for existing engineer officers. The majority of the committee favoured giving them military or command standing, but a minority was strongly opposed and insisted that their strong view should be published in the report. The consequence was that the report was never published and resolution of the issue was further delayed.

John Penn III was suffering from cancer and his health deteriorated in 1901 and 1902, yet despite this he gave an enthusiastic and delightful speech at a Horticultural Society lunch in response to a toast to his mother's recovery to health following an illness.[26] He was a natural speaker and carried his audience with him on most occasions. In October 1902 he collapsed while meeting at the House with a group of Nonconformists about the Education Bill. In 1903 he was absent from the House and he suggested to the Lewisham Conservatives that they should begin to consider finding another man as their next candidate. He died at his home in November 1903 at the age of fifty-five. His funeral was at St Margaret's, Lee and he was buried in the family vault. The list of attendees is long and contains the names of representatives from parliament, from many national and local organisations, men from the old John Penn and Sons factories of Thames Ironworks as well as members of the family. William Hartree II was there and no doubt the occasion took his mind back twenty-five years to the funeral of John Penn II and to that of his own father before. There was also a Memorial service at St Margaret's, Westminster, which was attended by the Prime Minister and Lady Balfour and many others from the House. The reports of the various speeches of remembrance show that he was well liked and respected by the people of Lewisham, Blackheath and Greenwich. The vicar of Lee said:

> Mr Penn could not help being kind, it was traditional in his nature and being, but he had gone on developing kindness, and rejoiced in the doing of kind acts unseen.[27]

A political opponent:

> ...we ought not to be denied the credit, also of the great respect – shared by all of us – for the truly English gentleman whom death has snatched from us at such an untimely age.[28]

The mayor of Lewisham:

> Ever desirous to serve the borough, always responsive to an appeal, ever willing to listen to any inhabitant of the borough, he had been an excellent representative in parliament.[29]

A biography of his son-in-law, G. F. S. Bowles, left a rather shallow and partial picture. John Penn III's clubs are mentioned – Turf, Windhams and Marlborough – and then the comment:

> ...a good shot – typical of upbringing and schooling, given to outdoor, rather than academic pursuits, but by no means stupid.[30]

His public record shows there was much more to him that that. His estate was valued at just under £200,000.

Ellen Penn died at The Cedars in November 1911 after a short illness. Her funeral was also at St Margaret's, Lee. William Hartree II was there for a Penn funeral again. She was remembered for all her good works, several of which have already been described but most of which go unrecorded. She supported charitable institutions in the district and had never-failing kindness to the poor.

> No one who appealed to her for help – and she knew it was a genuine case – was turned away empty handed. Her unseen charity abounded at every hand; it was her pleasure to relieve honest poverty and to mitigate by generous gifts the distress of the afflicted and bereaved.[31]

This is very similar to some of the writing about her husband, whose almoner she was. The vicar of St Nicholas, Deptford spoke of her in similar words and said he knew of 'No one to take her place'. In her will she made bequests to her two personal servants and two gardeners of £100 each; to four gardeners of £150 each; and to all the domestic servants £5 for each year of service up to ten and £10 for each year beyond. There were charitable bequests to the Miller Hospital and Royal Kent dispensary in Greenwich Road (£3,000); to Workshops for the Blind in South Street, Greenwich (£2,000) and to St John's Hospital, Lewisham (£2,000). There were itemised bequests of valuable objects to her children and two granddaughters. A portrait of John Penn was left to the Almshouses in South Street, Greenwich (Plate Ia). A sum of £1,000 went to each trustee. The residue and the funds from her life interest, marriage and post-nuptial settlements were to be shared by her surviving children and two granddaughters. The probate valuation was £193,400.

Frank Penn died at Dover in 1916 with an estate valued at £981. William Penn died in London in 1921 with an estate valued at £164,000; no obituary or memoir has been found. William Hartree II died in 1928.

Note about boilers and draught

In a water-tube boiler the water is inside tubes which are heated by the hot gases from the fire swirling past them. The tubes are long and of small diameter so the heating area is large in relation to the volume of water, hence the water is heated quickly. There were various boiler designs with different arrangements of tubes and different ways to clean or replace them. The cylindrical boiler did not provide the high heating area to volume relationship and so was less efficient but, because it did not have all the tube end joints, it was simpler to build and maintain. For boiler pressures above 150 psi, it was evident that once the practical problems had been solved the water-tube boiler would be preferred. Until they were solved the choice was a matter of opinion.

A good draught through the fire was necessary for efficient combustion of the coal. There were two ways to achieve this. One was to induce a greater draught up the funnel and the other was to raise the pressure of the air in the stokehold where the stokers worked and force the air in under the grate. The latter required the stokehold to have double pressure doors for men's entry and exit. The pressurised zone could include the coal bunkers, not a convenient arrangement. Again the choice between the two systems was a matter of opinion.

7. UNDER NEW MANAGEMENT (1899–1911)

For many years John Penn and Sons had supplied engines for ships built by Thames Ironworks and Shipbuilding. That company had its yard on the north shore of the Thames at the point where the River Lea, here known as Bow Creek, enters the Thames opposite the north bend of the Greenwich peninsula (001, Area Map, p8). It was from this yard that Thomas Ditchburn, with C. J. Mare, had worked with John Penn II on the *Fairy* and the other projects. During the Russian War C. J. Mare had taken on some low-cost contracts which led to the bankruptcy of the yard. His father-in-law took over the business and in 1857 re-formed it as Thames Iron Works and Shipbuilding. The yard was on both banks of Bow Creek, which provided plenty of space but with a rather inconvenient layout. The Middlesex bank site was of only five acres and held the offices, plumbers' shop and timber yard. The Essex bank site was of twenty acres and, according to Barry, well laid out.

In 1863, after building HMS *Warrior*, the company was in financial difficulty and reformed its capital structure again, this time as Thames Iron Works, Shipbuilding, Engineering and Dry Dock Co Ltd.[1] Its financial difficulties returned in the slump of the 1870s and 80s. The name changed again in 1871 and 1872, leaving it as Thames Ironworks and Shipbuilding Co Ltd. The yard's history included other major ironwork contracts than ships; for example, the ironwork for Brunel's Saltash and Stephenson's Menai Strait bridges, many dock gates and sluices for dams. Their Civil Engineering Department was still in this line of work. They had recently gone into electrical engineering for both marine and land use with some success but there is no doubt that shipbuilding was the core business. Their fortunes improved again with the increased orders from the Navy which sustained them through the 1890s. The Chairman of Thames Ironworks was Arnold F. Hills, who was a rather unconventional entrepreneur. He had some rather fine human relations ideals but found it very difficult to make effective use of them in the real world of business. The Good Fellowship profit-sharing scheme, introduced in 1892, raised protest when times were hard.[2] He had supported the eight-hour-day claim by the union in 1897. Like most owner managers he was paternalistic and provided sports and social facilities for the employees. The Thames Ironworks' football club eventually became the club now known as West Ham United, which is still cheered on by its supporters as 'the Irons'. Also, although Thames Iron was a public company, Hills made sure that he maintained control of it through his own and his family's shares.

At Thames Ironworks' Annual General Meeting on 30 March 1899 it was reported that

> So great has been the pressure of Engineering orders that the Directors have made arrangements for taking over the famous works of John Penn & Sons.[3]

A letter of A. F. Hills dated 4 April shows that the purchase by Thames Ironworks and Shipbuilding took place that month. The price was not disclosed. It was proposed to form a new company, Thames Iron Works, Shipbuilding and Engineering Co Ltd. A capital restructuring was designed by Hambros to achieve this. It was to include funds for the modernisation of the works of John Penn and Sons. Hills envisaged something quite comprehensive.

> ...arrangements for the re-modelling of these works upon the most approved modern methods, and for their equipment with the best modern plant.

la Framed pastel portrait of John Penn II
lb Penn Almshouses, South Street, Greenwich, dedication stone

IIa Launch of HMS *Agamemnon*, 1852

IIb HMS *Devastation*, 1871

IIIa HMS *Warrior*, 1861

IIIb Replica double trunk engine, HMS *Warrior*, 2005

IVa Oscillating engine in *Diesbar*, 2005

IVb Gunboat engine from *Xantho*, 2007

He must have judged that there was a lot to do to bring the plant up to current standards. This financing scheme for the new company was toned down in the prospectus and funds to carry out a comprehensive modernisation did not become available from the new capital structure. Although *The Economist* reported that 'The undertaking is a high-class industrial', in reality Thames's, and Penn's, shaky financial record and Hills's determination to retain control must have limited the amount Hambros judged it sensible to try to raise. It seems that the reporter did not appreciate the two companies' situations, with their works trapped in uncompetitive locations. Hills was to be the chairman of the new company and William Penn joined the board as a director.

There was some investment at Greenwich and Deptford.[4] A major project was a new works on the lower end of the Greenwich site to make the components of Belleville boilers. This followed Maudslay, who had acquired rights from Belleville in 1893 and built a plant on its Greenwich site. It was, however, before the parliamentary committee (see Chapter 6) had reached its conclusions. Another project was the installation of a steam-driven electricity generator. The electricity was used for lighting, for machine drives in the new shop and to operate the cranes in both new and old shops. In the old large machining and erecting shop there were frequent lifts of pieces of 10 to 12 tons in weight. The conversion of the cranes from hand operation to electric drive reduced handling times from thirty to ten minutes and labour needs from eight men to two. The Belleville boiler plant would not have had John Penn III's support but it is hard to understand why the Penn management had not introduced some electrification. They may have realised that much more drastic action was needed and that they could not afford to take it, and so had just let the firm drift slowly downwards. 'Penn's Greenwich' remained the telegraphic address.

William Penn resigned from the board by April 1901, on grounds of ill health. His place was taken by George S. Young, the Manager of the Engineering Department, who was responsible for the modernisation of Penn's shops and for bringing them into the Thames Ironworks company culture, including the Good Fellowship profit sharing scheme, in which Hills and the board had great faith.[5]

Although there were Navy contracts to complete, the Engineering Department was in need of new orders by the end of 1901. The Belleville boilers for HMS *Duncan*, *Albemarle* and *Cornwallis* had been finished that year. In service Belleville boilers did not live up to the promise shown in trials and these were the only Belleville-fitted ships Thames made. They also built a large Orloff colour printing machine, which it was hoped might lead to a new line of business. It did not.

In 1903 the firm received a contract from the Admiralty to build HMS *Black Prince*. She was to have a sister ship, the *Duke of Edinburgh*, for which the contract had gone elsewhere. The Admiralty required that the two were to have parts which 'were to be interchangeable in every possible particular'. This had never before been attempted on so large a scale and needed the installation of a very complete and accurate gauging system in the works. It was certainly much more than the Admiralty requirement during the Crimean War. HMS *Black Prince* was sunk during the Battle of Jutland in 1916.

Despite the *Black Prince* contract there was still a lack of work in the Engineering Department. At this time road transport and the motor industry were in their infancy. Thames saw this as a new business opportunity. A steam lorry design was developed and a prototype built with the hope that it would be able to compete in the market. The first lorry was completed early in 1904 and another soon after, as well as a twenty-hundredweight petrol van. These were exhibited at two shows in 1905.[6] Thames then built a new Motor Works on the lower level of the Greenwich site and made a substantial investment in modern machine tools to equip it.

There was more attention to the motor business in 1906 with the development of cars and omni-buses. The chassis and engines were entirely made at the Greenwich works. Bodywork was done separately by specialist body builders. A West End Agency and Garage were established for the Thames range of motor vehicles.[7] This was looked upon as an important new line of business for the company, but it was just too small in relation to shipbuilding to make a significant impression on the overall financial result. Thames had a stand at the Olympia Motor Show in 1906.

There were no new Navy orders in 1906 and 1907. A welcome contract came from the Metro-politan Water Board for pumping engines to be installed at the Walton pumping station. They are still in place but not used. A 1904 order for compound engines for ten paddle steamers for the London County Council was still in hand.[8] It had been placed with Thames despite a lower cost bid from a firm in the north. These two local, public authority customers were supporting local industry.

There were still no Admiralty orders in 1908 and Hills was sure this was all because the 'Ring' of shipyards in the North, associated with steelworks which produced armour plate, was combining to put him out of business. Thames made a loss. The following year, 1909 was another bleak one and then, early in 1910, the company obtained the contract for HMS *Thunderer*, which was to be com-pleted in two years.[9] With 27,000 ihp, she was the most powerful of the three turbine-engined ships they built. At the 1910 AGM it was reported that the Engineering department was busy with the *Thunderer* contract, which implies that the Greenwich works was building the Parsons turbines, the most modern marine steam engines of the day. Thus the Greenwich Works saw the whole marine steam story from side-lever engines in 1825 to Parsons turbines eighty-five years later.

In January 1910 a Special General Meeting was held to agree on financing for the *Thunderer* con-tract. At the AGM in 1911 the future seemed bright with the *Thunderer* well in hand and motor orders coming in well. However, immediately after there was an Extraordinary General Meet-ing of the preference shareholders regarding a Second Mortgage debenture offer to raise further funding to finance work in hand. It was agreed, but the financial weakness of the company was becoming more and more evident.

The company's 1911 *Historical Catalogue for the Empire Exhibition* includes the range of cars and a personal testimonial by William Penn of Taverham Hall, Norfolk; he still owned some shares. It shows him to have had an engineer's appreciation of the vehicle.

> I have been greatly pleased with the running of my 60hp, 6 cylinder Thames. It runs beautifully smooth and very quietly, both at fastest and slowest speeds, and with a large limousine body is an easy car to drive, on top direct drive anything from forty-five miles to a slow, crawling speed in traffic.

> My Thames cab is also a great success. The way it pulls up a hill with passengers and luggage is quite wonderful for a two cylinder engine. The worm drive gives very smooth quiet running.

My man drove it down to London on an occasion three months ago, and he tells me that in the run of one hundred and twenty miles, petrol used worked out at twenty-six miles to the gallon. He also tells me that during the past four weeks, when Mrs. Penn was with the cab in London, he found he could turn around in Dover Street, and other small streets, where ordinary cabs could not get round without reversing. Yours truly,[10]

This was before the days of the London cab with a tight turning circle.

The catalogue price for the fifty-horsepower 6-cylinder model chassis and engine was £735 and for a limousine body £125. The sixty-horsepower model did a speed trial of three and a half hours at nearly 90mph.

By this time Thames was the only major yard building ships on the Thames. Thorneycroft and Yarrow, which made their own engines for their specialised ranges of high-speed vessels, had already moved to Southampton and the Clyde. The engineers Maudslay had gone out of business in 1904 and Humphreys, Tenant & Dykes in 1908. Hills was not prepared to face the reality that his cost structure could not compete with the yards in the north. He was a past master at appeals for support from anyone who might listen and had had some success with the government. He was obsessed about the high London wages and he sought protection from their effect on government contracts. In 1911 matters came to a head.[11] The Admiralty had asked for tenders for two cruisers. Thames's bid was the highest, next came the northerners outside the 'Ring', and then the 'Ring' as the lowest.

Winston Churchill, as First Lord of the Admiralty, was not prepared to ask Parliament to accept the highest bid in order to maintain a high-cost London yard. Immediately, local MPs and mayors tried to put pressure on the Admiralty to provide their constituencies with work but Churchill 'felt compelled to intimate that the outlook for Thames was not promising'.[12] A great demonstration was organised in Trafalgar Square and attended by ten thousand East Enders. In November 1911 Thames's bankers declined to honour the company's cheques. There were rumours of possible takeovers by a non-Ring northern yard but they came to nothing. The company went into receivership and the Admiralty could not place a contract with a company in that state. HMS *Thunderer*, by then being finished at Dagenham, was taken over by the Admiralty.[13] In December 1912 the works were closed. Hills tried again to raise a reconstruction fund but no one believed in him or it.

701 HMS *Thunderer*, 1911

In May 1913 the ex-Penn sites and machinery were put up for sale by auction.[14] The sale was scheduled to last six days and the catalogue listed over two thousand lots. The auctioneers, Fuller, Horsey, Sons & Cassell, highlighted four hundred lots as ones that would specially attract buyers. Of these one hundred and twenty-five were items other than machine tools; that is cranes, electric motors and equipment, steam plant and eighteen finished vans. Some two hundred and fifty highlighted lots were modern machine tools in the Motor Works on the Lower Level. The four 'nearly new' lots were, surprisingly, in the old shops. None of the large home-built machine tools described in the visitors' reports of thirty or more years ago were in the catalogue. They had become obsolete. Lots which are of nostalgic interest to the story were: the library of eighteen hundred volumes, presumably the workers' Reading Room; a 12in x 18in grasshopper engine, presumably that made by John Penn II in 1822; models of ships' engines, now in the Institution of Mechanical Engineers and Science Museum; some old harnesses and an oat mill in the garage, which had been the stables; two telegraph instruments; an Aveling Porter traction engine; the car engine which had achieved the Brooklands two-hundred-and-fifty-mile record. For the marine engineering workshops this is a very similar picture to that of the 1908 sale of Maudslay's Lambeth works – that of a tired old place, in truth obsolete in machinery, layout and handling facilities. Penn's Greenwich site was sold to a Deptford engineering firm, Messrs Defries, for £28,000. At that time industrial sites did not sell for retail or residential redevelopment. This came more than fifty years later in Greenwich and is still awaited in Deptford.

An interesting tailpiece comes from the Hoyt Metal Company magazine *The Notched Ingot* of March 1958. The writer records a conversation with an elderly friend who recalled walking down a street in Greenwich in 1912 or 13 and noticing that some machinery was on view prior to sale. He entered the premises and realised he was in the works which had once been famous as those of John Penn and Sons. He went into the light and lofty erecting shop and noticed the large drilling machine which had been installed so that one of the huge timber uprights of the building had been strapped to the lower part of the pillar of the drill, which took the weight on its base. He remembered seeing neatly stacked piles of used cutting tools by the machines. He remembered the foundry as rather cramped and left just as it must have been on the completion of the last job. He was puzzled by the number of brass finishers' lathes in the small turnery. There was a rusty old traction engine standing outside.

702 Pattern Shop, Greenwich site, 1950s

8. Conclusion

John Penn I had started his business in Greenwich in 1799. In 1843 he left it in good financial and technical shape to his son John Penn II. John Penn II expanded it and established it as a firm of high reputation for the quality of its products and as the major supplier of engines to the Royal Navy (Appendix 3, p122). He, and his partners William Hartree and John Matthew, set themselves up with lifestyles in keeping with the expectations of the times. John Penn II brought up his sons in a manner suitable to the family's status and made the elder two sons partners in the business. They, in turn, established themselves with appropriate lifestyles, as did the other family members. In the 1880s business conditions worsened and in 1899 they had to sell the business if anything was to survive. One hundred years of continuous activity on the same site, and mostly in the same business, is a remarkable achievement for any firm, especially a family-owned one. Amongst the Victorian Thameside shipbuilding and marine engineering firms there were only three which survived for three generations and a hundred years; they were Maudslay, Penn and Rennie (see Appendix 3, p122). Maudslay closed on Thameside in 1904 and at the time two family members set up in the new motor industry in Coventry; one as Maudslay and the other as the Standard Motor Company. Both were absorbed into larger groups in the second half of the 1900s.

Did the Penns do something wrong? Did they make a major business error? Could they have done something different and saved the business? To ascribe the failure to some 'third generation' generalisation is too facile. Each failure has its particular circumstances.

Entrepreneurial firms often become undercapitalised. They can borrow within limits but they cannot raise much capital whilst the owners retain control, which is usually a prime objective. Retained profits are their best source of capital. However, retained profits cannot be used for personal lifestyle. Choices have to be made. Whether to spend on new machines, new buildings, developing new products, relocation of the business or on a bigger house, some works of art, a yacht, a golf course or whatever. Which would provide the most personal satisfaction, both now and later? Of course entrepreneurs look beyond the short term, but it is hard to look far when good profits are being earned.

The Penns chose to make considerable personal expenditures for lifestyle in the second fifty years, from The Cedars onwards. Could that money have saved the business? It is not possible to give an answer in financial terms but a consideration of their non-financial values can be helpful.

What was the business aim of the Penn family? To be a leading supplier of marine engines; to operate the Greenwich and Deptford Works and employ all who worked there; or to be a source of personal money? From the story it seems to have been a combination of the second and third. The first is a detached, impersonal, corporate concept which is unlikely to have had much priority in their thinking.

The business became trapped in a location and on sites which had not been chosen or designed for marine engineering and which eventually made it uncompetitive. If John Penn II and his partners had seen this in the 1850s, when others gave the first warning, or John III and William had seen it in the 1870s or 80s, when the situation was relatively clear, could they have done anything?

Relocation is an expensive and risky undertaking. Financing must be found for the expenditure on a new site, for the new buildings and machinery and, at the same time, for continuing to run the business and meet the customers' needs. How many employees, those skilled servants of theirs, would have moved with the firm? The family would probably have felt that relocation would destroy the business as they knew it: as the employer of 'their men'.

It is hard to believe that relocation away from Thameside was ever a realistic option. Maudslay had tried partial relocation but it did not save them. Nearly all the Thameside shipbuilding and marine engineering firms reached this situation and collapsed. Yarrow and Thorneycroft both relocated to fulfil their more focused business missions. They had the ability to finance the moves, which were not without difficulties. The Thorneycroft name is the only one which still lives in the national scene, in Vosper-Thorneycroft, now just VT, Shipbuilding.

This has been the story of a family and its business told in the historical context. The context started with the perception of Britain as a maritime power presented in the Painted Hall of the Royal Naval Hospital in the early 1700s. At the end of the story, nearly two hundred years later, Britain was still the leading seaborne commercial empire, although much more imperial. She was still protected by the power of the Royal Navy, technologically transformed. She was still governed by a sovereign parliament, with a membership more representative of the new urban population. She was still ruled by a Protestant constitutional monarch. For all these similarities she was a very different place to live in. Industrialisation, urbanisation and technological change had arrived in full measure.

801 John Penn, Elbe steamer, modernisation of 1913

Author's Postscript

In my preface I explained how my industrial management career gave me an interest in industrial history which became one of the stimuli to write this story. As I was writing I realised that all the business situations and decisions I was describing were familiar to me – 'I've been there.'

Richard Hartree,

Sibford Ferris, 2007

Penn Family Tree II

(Descendants of John Penn ii mentioned in the Epilogue)

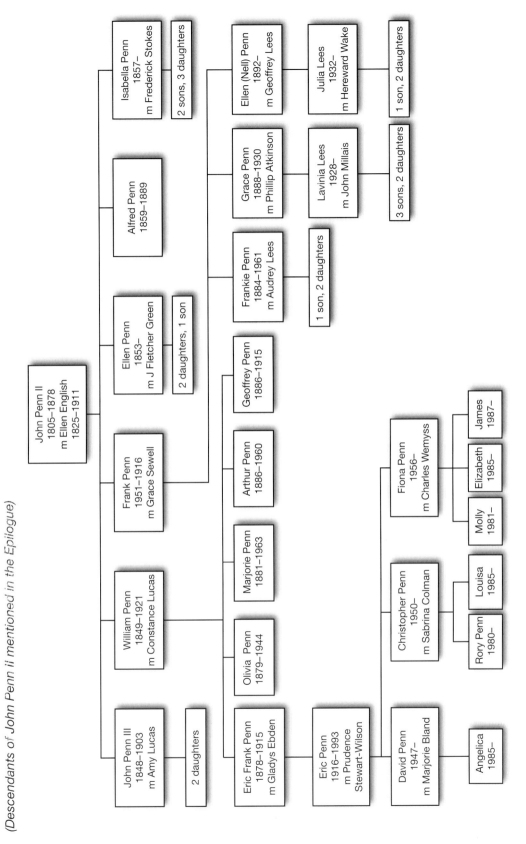

Epilogue by Prudence Penn

In 1947 I married the great grandson of John Penn II, and on taking their name became deeply interested in the family and its earlier generations. Penn's place in engineering and maritime history is significant and secure, but there was no record of the story of the family thereafter. Early in his researches Richard Hartree approached me and we decided to collaborate to write the full story. I hold various family documents which have been an invaluable resource in my research over the years. Richard's investigations have been even more wide-ranging. He has written the story of the firm and of the family as owners and managers. In this Epilogue I shall tell more about them as a family, bringing their story up to the present day and telling of their long service in the Households of the Royal Family. The Penn family tree on page 103 shows the individuals who appear in this narrative.

The Cedars in Blackheath was the family home of John II and Ellen's children, and continued later on to be an important place for their grandchildren. John and Ellen's six children, four boys and two girls, were born between 1849 and 1857. A family of that size was not unusual in those days. Their eldest son, John III, was eight years old when they moved into The Cedars. The younger children were William, Frank, Alfred, Ellen and Isabella, the youngest and the only one of the family to be born in the house. The children, therefore, from an early age grew up at The Cedars (formerly known as Lee Grove) an eighteenth-century mansion at Lee in Blackheath. The house was purchased by their father in 1856 from the executors of Thomas Brandram for £30,000, a pricey sum at that time. He renamed it *The Cedars* on account of the very fine cedars of Lebanon planted there at the turn of the century.

901 Lee Grove (or Place), early 1800s

The property included fifty-five acres of land which had been acquired by the previous owner, who had bought up surrounding fields as they became available, thereby creating parkland and a lake. The lake was achieved by enlarging and diverting the small stream known as Wricklemarsh Brook, which ran in approximately the same position as the present Blackheath to Lewisham railway. Extensive modernisation and building works were carried out by Penn, even to the extent of altering the course of the road outside the property to accommodate a lodge and a convenient in–and–out drive.

The Cedars was typical of a large family house of that time, dominated by a very hard-working father who spent his days at the engineering works in Bath Street, now named John Penn Street, or at the boiler works on the river at Deptford. He also had commissions in Europe which inevitably involved travelling abroad. The house was full of clutter: marble statues, potted plants, tables heavily draped with fringed velvet cloths and laden with photographs and other objects. There was a considerable collection of modern pictures and other symbols of Victorian affluence. All of this is visible in contemporary photographs. The property included a stable of horses and carriages, and extensive pleasure grounds with greenhouses and a walled garden.

This is the setting in which the family was brought up. The boys were sent to Harrow for the last two years of their schooling and the girls were educated at home with governesses. Ellen was a very loving and attentive mother, but they were possibly a little in awe of their father. Their second son William, later known as Bill, wrote to his mother in his Sunday letter from the Revd F. W. Farrer's house (Small House) at Harrow:

> Please send my skates if you have not already packed them off.
> How is papa? I must write to him, but I never know what to say to him, he would not take any interest in anything that I could think of.

This is a sad indication of the relationship at that time between father and son, but possibly not unusual in formal Victorian family life. Evidently he found it easier to communicate with his mother. In another letter William affectionately reprimands her for arriving late at Lord's to watch the Eton and Harrow cricket match:

> Dear Mother,
>
> I am sorry to say that I shall not be able to come home with you on Thursday night.
> Shall you go up to Lords on Friday or Saturday, or both or what?
> Mind you show up a great deal earlier than last time, because don't you remember we could not get the carriage in...
> I remain, my dear Mother,
> Your affectionate son
>
> William Penn

William played cricket for Harrow in the match against Eton in 1867.

As a small boy he sent a charming little unpunctuated Christmas letter from the nursery to his elder brother in the schoolroom, written on very small special pink paper with a robin on a branch in the snow printed at the top. The bird is holding a card in his beak saying 'Merry Christmas to you':

> My dear old John
>
> I hope you are quite well I am going to send all of you a letter do you not think the little bird pretty you see he says A Merry Christmas to you I think it is very pretty myself I am going to send Frank one and Elly [sister Ellen?] one and Dick one and Baby [Isabella] one I wonder what Baby will make of hers a 'gibb a gibb a jar I serpose' [sic]
> I remain your affectionate Brother
>
> W Penn

Sunday worship was regular. St Margaret's Church at Lee is situated across the road from The Cedars and the Penn family would have walked to attend services there, sometimes twice a day. It is recorded in church records that John Penn paid for new oak pews to replace the old stalls throughout the church; they remain to this day.

Many distinguished visitors came to the house: artists, musicians and business associates of John II. The former Emperor Napoleon III and his wife the Empress Eugenie visited in 1872. They had purchased Camden Place near Chislehurst in Kent where Queen Victoria visited them and described it as 'that small house' and referred to 'the poor Emperor's humble little rooms'. In fact, though, the house had twenty rooms apart from the domestic quarters and they lived there with their family and a staff of no fewer than twenty-three servants – hardly an insignificant dwelling.

The Cedars was a bustling house full of family and servants and constant visitors. (The census of 1881, three years after the death of John II, recorded sixteen members of the family and twenty-one servants in the house.) There was music and there were books and John Penn spoke several languages, which is remarkable for a man who left school at the age of thirteen. He was an accomplished musician and played the organ that he had installed in the house. He had formed his own band and gave concerts to raise funds for local charities.

John Penn III, the eldest of John and Ellen's children, was educated at Harrow School and at Trinity College, Cambridge. Following that he did a three-year apprenticeship with the family firm, and went on to work there. His brother William also joined the firm and they became partners with their father in 1872 and took over the management in 1875.

In 1876 John III married Amy Lucas, daughter of Thomas Lucas Esq., later first Baronet of Ashtead Park in Surrey. They lived in a large house in Carlton House Terrace and they had two daughters. A year later in 1877 William (known as Bill) married Amy's younger sister Constance (Connie); they lived in Richmond Terrace in Westminster and had a family of five. There were three sons: Eric Frank, born 1878 and twin boys, Arthur and Geoffrey, born 1886. Their two daughters, Olive and Marjorie, were born in 1879 and 1881.

With John III and Amy having no male heir it came about that the direct line of the Penn family would be through the younger brother William and his successors.

Left: 903 Connie with twins, Arthur and Geoffrey, 1887

Right: 902 Connie with Eric Frank, 1888

I should also mention the other members of John II and Ellen's family. There was Frank, who was an accomplished amateur cricketer and sportsman. He played cricket for Kent 1875 to 1881 and for England in 1880. He married twice, first Grace Sewell, by whom, in 1884, he had a son, Frank II , known as Frankie, whom I remember well at Bawdsey Hall, his home in Suffolk when he was in his sixties and seventies, as an attractive and fine-looking man with a twinkling eye. He inherited his father's sporting skills, playing cricket for Kent and the Household Brigade in a match against the Royal Artillery in 1906. As the result of a hunting accident in his late fifties he was confined to a wheelchair until he died in 1961.

The three younger children of John II and Ellen were Alfred, who died unmarried in his thirties. Very little is known about him and why he died so young. After Alfred came their two daughters, Ellen II, who married Joseph Fletcher Green, and Isabella, who married Frederick Stokes, another sportsman who played cricket for Kent and captained England at rugby. Houses were built on The Cedars estate for both daughters on their marriages.

In 1889, when the firm became a limited company, John III was elected Chairman and he and William were the two major shareholders. In 1891 John III became the Conservative Member of Parliament for Lewisham and consequently during the 1890s much of his time was taken up with his parliamentary duties. He won the seat again in 1892 and held it for twelve years. His recreations were shooting and golf and he was more than competent at both. He rented Archerfield in East Lothian during the autumn recess for several years running, where there was excellent shooting and a private golf course in the grounds. There are family photographs of house parties at Archerfield, where he invited family and parliamentary friends as his guests. His golfing ability enabled him to become a 'leading Parliamentary golfer'.

904 John Penn III,
at Archerfield, 1890s

William and Connie moved to Taverham Hall in Norfolk in 1894 and in the 1890s William's eldest son, Eric Frank, spent time with his grandmother at The Cedars during his Easter holiday from Eton. His diary entries give a fascinating picture of the grounds and his interest in birds.

Friday 6th March 1896
Went up to the Cedars by the 11.00 train from Taverham and got there at about 4.30. Most comfortable journey – a saloon with a compartment communicating which Miss Moffat and the twins (his brothers Arthur and Geoffrey) went in. Mother, Pop and Pip and I in the saloon. The Frank Penns and Dorothy and Joan (daughters of John Penn III) at the Cedars.

Sunday 22nd March 1896
Bird nesting in the morning, by the pond in the afternoon. Plenty of Thrushes and some Blackbirds. Also a few Sparrow's nests. A solitary pair of Rooks have built on the cottage side of the pond just at the top of Runaway Hill. Probably young birds kicked out of the Rookery proper. Aunt Grace heard the Chiff Chaff here today for the first time. To Church in the

evening where we had some <u>very</u> bad music which lasted too long. Plovers eggs Leadenhall market 10d. each.

Easter Sunday 22nd March 1896
Church in the morning. Bird nesting in the afternoon. Church with Aunt Grace in the evening. Put off going to Taverham.

Bill and Connie's eldest son Eric Frank, the father-in-law I never met, was a very tall, good-looking man. He was educated at Eton and went up to Trinity College, Cambridge in 1897. He was a first-class cricketer, playing in the Eton eleven. In 1898 he visited America with P. F. Warner's team. He became a cricket 'blue' in 1899 and played in the Varsity Match again in 1901. He also played in one match for England in South Africa.

After Cambridge he worked for a time in a bill broking firm in the City. He had fought in the South African war with the Royal Scots, later joining the Grenadier Guards in the Great War. He was a keen and proficient shot, and a knowledgeable ornithologist. He loved the country and the life it had to offer.

Eric Frank's uncle, John Penn MP, died in 1903 at the early age of fifty-four after a short illness and his funeral was at St Margaret's, Lee, close to The Cedars, where he was buried beside his father in the family vault. His funeral and his memorial service in St Margaret's, Westminster are fully described in Richard's text.

The family home of Eric Frank's bride, Gladys Ebden, was in Lanarkshire but, probably for the convenience of the family and their guests, they were married at St Paul's Church, Knightsbridge in London on 25 April 1906. His parents, Bill and Connie, had recently gone to the South of France for a

905 Eric Frank at the nets, Cambridge, 1900

holiday, where Connie became ill. Sadly she was advised not to travel back to England for the wedding and they both wrote of their deep regret and sadness. It was also an immense disappointment for their son and his new wife.

The newly married couple moved into a large house on the south side of Gloucester Square, from where Eric Frank worked as a bill broker in the City. Coincidentally, when their son Eric married me in 1947 our first home was number 33 Gloucester Square, one of the new houses which had been built at each end of the square in the 1930s.

They spent holidays at Newton House near Elvanfoot in Lanarkshire, the home of Gladys's parents, Charles Ebden (known within the family as 'The Purple Emperor') and his wife Agnes. It was a charming eighteenth-century house situated on the banks of the upper waters of the River Clyde with excellent shooting rights. Newton later became a joint inheritance between my husband Eric and his uncle Thomas Ebden, who continued to live there with his wife. They had no children and consequently after the death of Thomas in the early 1950s Eric, who was about to embark with his regiment to Tripoli in North Africa, sold Newton to a local man who it transpired only wanted it for the land, and allowed the house to fall into disrepair and eventually a ruin. It stands close to what is now the M74 motorway, and whenever we passed we watched it crumbling away wall by wall into what is now a grassy mound. This was painful for Eric who had spent so many very happy holidays there as a boy.

Eric Frank and his wife Gladys, in the early years of their marriage, often visited his elderly grandmother at The Cedars. Ellen was twenty years younger than her husband and survived him through a widowhood of thirty-three years. She died at The Cedars in 1911. Ellen had cared actively for the local people and particularly for those who had worked in the family firm. She was greatly loved and much respected and she is commemorated by a marble plaque on the north wall inside St Margaret's Church, Lee, inscribed with the words:

906 Ellen at 80

IN LOVING MEMORY OF ELLEN PENN
WIFE OF JOHN PENN of the CEDARS, LEE
DIED 25TH NOVEMBER 1911 AGED 86

She was buried in the family vault which stands close to the north-west corner of the church and contained the remains of John II and their sons Alfred and John III.

Ellen's death ended a chapter of a family who had progressed in two generations from humble beginnings to the owners of a substantial and prosperous business. The family had thrived through the ingenuity and hard work of her husband and of his father before him, the millwright from Bridgwater in Somerset. It is fully recorded in this book how John Penn I travelled to London as a young man to find employment using the skills that he had learned in his youth, and how he established his own thriving business in Greenwich.

In 1912 William and Connie, with their two unmarried daughters Olive and Marjorie and the twins Arthur and Geoffrey, moved from Taverham Hall Norfolk into 34 Wilton Crescent. Arthur had completed his studies at Cambridge and was continuing with law in the Inner Temple. Theirs was an exceptionally happy and united family. They shared a unique sense of the ridiculous and delighted in each other's company. This has been passed down in a strangely similar way to later generations. When the War came in 1914 their comfortable life was to be shattered, as happened with so many families.

All three boys, and their cousin Frankie, joined the army and fought in the 1914–1918 War. Geoffrey served in the Rifle Brigade and in February 1915 was killed in action. In May of that year his twin, Arthur, who was serving with the Grenadier Guards in France, was wounded. Then in October Eric Frank, also a Grenadier, was killed in action. These were devastating losses for the family, especially for Gladys who was soon to give birth to their first child.

Connie was a very beautiful woman and with a strength of character that undoubtedly helped her to overcome the loss of two sons in that short space of time. Her husband William wrote to her in her grief:

2nd January 1916
St. Albans Court, Dover

My own darling, my beautiful and good darling. Your letter this morning with the few short brave words was by far the finest thing I have ever read, and could only have been written by a loving mother and wife, with the greatest and bravest heart that could be carried in a human frame...and I do so love to see that you say 'I don't think we have done too badly.'

Arthur had recorded his unfortunate encounter with the enemy in his Game Book in his own inimitable style:

May 17th 1915
Place: Richebourg, La Quinque Rue
Number of guns: Plenty
Bag: under various, Self
Total: 1
Notes: Rain, late start, quarry picked up with both legs down.

He was awarded the Military Cross and mentioned in dispatches.

The following year he wrote a letter to his father:

Oct. 25.1916
My dear father,

...I wouldn't have missed the opportunity of taking my humble share in it (the war).

All my life thanks to the wonderful kindness of two unequalled parents, and, to a far lesser degree, of many incomparable friends, I have enjoyed such amazing happiness that at all times I have felt at the back a sort of uneasiness because I was giving nothing in return...I feel so sorry for the boys who join the army nowadays fresh from school, for they can never know all the glorious days I have had since I left Eton seven years ago.

As I write they come flocking back to me – memories of Cambridge and of summer days at Taverham and in Scotland – of shooting parties all over England – country houses full of the most splendid friends that ever man was blessed with. Many of them have gone ahead, but the memory of their companionship is a possession of which I cannot be cheated...I could never tell you and mother what love and admiration and gratitude I feel towards you both.

There never was a pair like you, and that's the truth.

All my love

Arthur

Gladys was devastated by her husband's early death and the prospect of bringing up their unborn child on her own was a daunting one. Following the birth of her son Eric on 9 February 1916, Gladys moved to a house in Beaufort Gardens off Brompton Road. As the only grandchild he was adored by William and Connie and became the direct line of the Penn family. His happy relationship with his paternal grandfather sadly ended with William's death in 1921. This left his uncle Arthur as his closest male relation.

907 Connie with grandson Eric, 1916

908 William and Eric at 34, Wilton Crescent, 1920

909 William and Eric, 1921, 'sense of the ridiculous'

Later Eric went to Summerfields preparatory school near Hastings, close to Baldslow Place, the home of his maternal grandparents and where he spent his holidays. They also owned Newton House in Lanarkshire already mentioned where he also visited, usually with his mother and sometimes with his two aunts, and Arthur came there to shoot in August or September. At this time his closest Penn family contemporaries were the second cousins who were the children of Frankie and his sister Nell.

Frankie Penn and his sister Nell were the second generation of the family to marry siblings when they married Audrey and Geoffrey Lees of Falcutt House in Northamptonshire. The first had been John III and William Penn when they married Amy and Connie Lucas. And then, after skipping a generation, it has happened for a third time in the present generation. Two of the daughters of Julia (Lees) and her husband Sir Hereward (Toby) Wake have married two brothers, Roddy and Adam Fleming, the sons of Richard Fleming.

At the age of sixteen Eric suffered an emotionally devastating blow with the death of his mother from cancer. He was at Eton at the time and was immediately embraced by the Penn family, who welcomed him into his grandmother's house in Wilton Crescent close to Hyde Park, where his uncle Arthur and his two aunts Olive and Marjorie still lived. His uncle Arthur became an exceptional and greatly loved surrogate father to him. They had a wonderful relationship and were devoted to one another. Arthur had been educated at Eton and went up to Trinity College, Cambridge, in October 1905 where he studied Law. He had practised as a barrister before joining King and Shaxson, a bill broking firm in the City, of which he subsequently became chairman, and remained as a director after leaving the firm. He was a meticulous administrator who was always considerate and supportive of his staff, and his unique sense of humour enhanced everything that he did throughout his life.

He was a man of many talents with an irresistible charm. He never married and had more time for his friends and their children than he might otherwise have done. He accumulated a wide circle of friends, and being a first-class shot and entertaining company he was asked to stay in many of the great houses of England and Scotland. His meticulously written and delightfully illustrated Game Books testify to this.

His letters, many of which were kept by his friends, were elegantly written and invariably illustrated. After his death many people suggested that we should make a collection of them for private circulation. We never did, suspecting, probably rightly, that he would not have approved.

Glamis Castle was one of the places that Arthur visited on several occasions in the 1920s and he became a lifelong friend of Elizabeth Bowes-Lyon. He was probably first invited by Elizabeth's brothers, with whom he was at Eton. A deep friendship with the family was established then and lasted until his death in 1960. After Elizabeth's marriage to the Duke of York, and subsequently on his accession in 1937, the King appointed Arthur a Groom in Waiting in his first Household.
He acted as private secretary to the Queen and was also her treasurer during the war years, combining these duties with those of Regimental Adjutant Grenadier Guards, across the road at Wellington Barracks. In wartime a particularly important job. The person in this post is being

911 Arthur Penn at Drumlanrig

910 Elizabeth Bowes Lyon,
The Duke of York and Arthur Penn, 1923

responsible for liaising with the families of guardsmen in the event of their being wounded, taken prisoner or being killed in action. His caring and compassionate character made him eminently suited to this position.

Connie died in March 1942 at the age of eighty-seven, mercifully two years before her eldest daughter Olive was killed in the Guards Chapel when it was hit by a flying bomb at 11.30 on the morning of Sunday 18 June 1944. Arthur was about to leave Buckingham Palace to go to Windsor to see the Queen when he heard of the tragedy, and was on the scene within moments and able to identify his sister.

After the death of the King in 1952 Arthur continued to serve the Queen, who now became known as Queen Elizabeth The Queen Mother, as her Treasurer, and he moved with her to Clarence House on The Mall, which had been the first home of her daughter The Princess Elizabeth and The Duke of Edinburgh after their marriage in 1947. He played a vital part in the logistics of the move to Clarence House, and the acquisition of some of the furniture for her new home. The alterations to Birkhall, her home close to Balmoral in Aberdeenshire, and the acquisition and alterations to the Castle of Mey in Caithness were also overseen by Arthur.

He had a discerning eye and impeccable taste in furniture, clocks and china, and recorded his own purchases in an immaculate book, giving the description, the provenance when known, and the price paid – never very much at the time but always of superior quality and taste. The first entry in the book in January 1911 is for a walnut hanging mirror for which he paid six pounds. The final entry is in August 1960, four months before his death. He paid seventy pounds for a wooden jardinière decorated on a black ground with Chinese figures and lacquered.

In 1945, after the war, Arthur and his sister Marjorie bought Sternfield, a former Queen Anne Vicarage near Saxmundham in Suffolk, where he was able to house his lifelong collection of furniture, pictures, clocks and china. And they created a beautiful garden. He was a true countryman and, enjoying shooting as he did, he trained his own black Labrador dogs. They had sensible working dog names, such as Teal, Snipe and Shadow, but his sister Marjorie invented her own ridiculous names for them: 'Satin Lips' and 'Rubber Toes' are two that I remember.

Arthur was never idle. He tried his hand at bricklaying, and he made walking sticks. First he selected and cut branches of hazel wood on his walks; these he straightened in a press in his workshop, and when ready he carved and polished the handles and gave them to his friends. He was a competent singer and belonged to a London madrigal society. He was a more than accomplished artist, and illustrated his letters and Game Books with sketches and watercolours.

He spent fifteen very happy years at Sternfield, the first home that he had owned in the country, and we and our children shared in this. Eric and I had become engaged to be married there in October of 1946. I think I was their first guest among the packing cases. Many years later one of our sons told me that as a child he had always thought that Arthur and his sister Marjorie were husband and wife.

When Arthur bought the house in 1945 he wrote in his diary: 'I have always wanted to live in Suffolk, I feel so well here that I could knock over a bus – and then eat it.'

Towards the end of 1960 Arthur's eyesight was deteriorating and he was at risk of losing an eye. He was admitted to hospital and died very suddenly on 30 December at the age of seventy-four.

The Queen Mother, in a letter to Arthur's sister from The Royal Lodge, her home in Windsor Great Park, wrote:

...I have tried once or twice to write to you, to try and tell you how eternally grateful I shall always be to Arthur for his wonderful support and unselfish and devoted service to me and my family. He was such a great and wise person and that he is no longer there, with his balanced and right advice on all the many problems that assail one, is a terrible loss.

Clarence House is certainly not the same place without him and he is continually missed by all of my Household and all the servants. He was so marvellous in always making himself available to listen to their troubles and perplexities, and with the wonderful mixture of fun and understanding of human nature with which he solved their problems, he always sent them away happy.

For myself, to be able to turn to Arthur for wise counsel in so many different situations, to be able to share the pleasure of beautiful things and to laugh, was something that has meant more to me than I can ever say, both in happy days and sad days.

How wonderful to have lived a life such as Arthur lived. Spreading gaiety and kindness around him, and goodness and courage as well. He was a great example in how to live on this earth.

Elizabeth R

His nephew Eric was fortunate to have been brought up and cared for by him, as also was I to have shared in his loving kindness. I was devoted to him.

The family had moved away from the world of engineering to one of law, wartime military service and the Royal Household. My husband, Eric, after Eton and Magdalene College, Cambridge, from 1935 to 1938, joined the Grenadier Guards as a regular soldier. He was 6ft 4ins tall, taking after his father, and was in The King's Company, where you were required to be over a certain height. With the outbreak of war in 1939 he went from performing ceremonial duties in London to active service. He fought in France, and was among those evacuated from Dunkirk. He served in the Italian campaign and ended the war in Austria, having been awarded a Military Cross in Italy.

Eric and I were married in London on 29 January 1947 at St Mark's Church in North Audley Street. It was a notoriously hard winter and it was a freezing cold day. Several of our Scottish guests were unable to travel south for the wedding on account of the weather. The Queen and Princess Elizabeth attended the service on the eve of their departure with the King and Princess Margaret on HMS *Vanguard* for a state visit to South Africa.

For the next thirteen years I 'followed the drum' to Tripoli in North Africa and then to Germany and London. During that time our three children, David, Christopher and Fiona (Weymyss) were born. In 1952, the year of The Queen's coronation, we bought number 30 Chelsea Square, a delightful house situated at the end of the communal square garden. It was a perfect place for a growing family and where our daughter was born in 1956.

The year 1960 was an important milestone for us. Arthur's death coincided with Eric being forced to leave his regiment after a back injury, and at the same time being considered for the post of Assistant Comptroller of The Lord Chamberlain's Office in the Queen's Household, a position to which he was appointed in that year. Coincidentally, in the same year our eldest son David, who was at Eton, was appointed a page of honour to The Queen. There are two pages who attend Her Majesty at the service in St. George's Chapel Windsor. They are dressed in scarlet frock coats with gold lace and cypher buttons over cream satin waistcoat and knee breeches. At the neck is a lace jabot and lace cuffs. They wear black patent leather shoes with cut steel buckles and red heels. A small sword hangs from a leather belt under the coat at the wrist which passes through an opening at the back of the coat from left to right.

Arthur had left Sternfield, his beautiful Queen Anne house and garden in Suffolk, to us, and after the death of his sister Marjorie in 1964 we invited the distinguished architect, Raymond Erith, who was a Suffolk man, to make alterations to increase the number of rooms, and to improve the outside appearance of the house, an operation performed with great skill and taste. The work was completed in 1966 and we lived there for the next twenty years. It was a happy house, and we entertained a great many family and friends during that time.

Eric was by then Comptroller of The Lord Chamberlain's Office and we lived between Suffolk and a crown property in Stable Yard, St James's Palace, having sold our house in Chelsea Square. The Lord Chamberlain's Office is responsible for the arrangements of many royal events in London,

912 David dressed as Page of Honour to The Queen, 1959

913 Eric at Horseguards Parade, after The Queen's Birthday 115 Parade 1961

Windsor and Edinburgh during the year, with a special interest in protocol and ceremonial. The office handles the two inward state visits by overseas Heads of State each year, and also Investitures, Garden Parties and the State Opening of Parliament. The services of the Orders of Chivalry and royal weddings and funerals are also handled by this department of the Queen's household.

The office is also responsible for some of the most ancient traditions connected with the monarchy. These include the Body Guards (Gentlemen at Arms, the Yeomen of the Guard and the Royal Company of Archers in Scotland), the Crown Jewels and The Queen's ownership of the swans on a stretch of the River Thames.

The Comptroller has the executive responsibility for the Lord Chamberlain's Office. All royal events necessarily require careful coordination and meticulous planning with other organisations such as the Foreign Office, Foreign Diplomatic Corps, the House of Lords, Westminster Abbey, St Paul's Cathedral, the Metropolitan Police, BBC Outside Broadcasting, the Household Brigade and the households and staff of other members of the Royal Family. Events are planned with great care many months in advance, and coordinating meetings are held in the state rooms of St James's Palace for this purpose with the Comptroller in the Chair.

Eric retired in 1982 after twenty-one years in the Lord Chamberlain's Office, during which time he had been responsible for, among other things, the arrangements for the weddings of Princess Margaret, Princess Alexandra and Princess Anne and the funerals of The Duke of Windsor, Sir Winston Churchill and Lord Mountbatten. In those years there were some forty state visits by foreign heads of state, and a similar number of garden parties at Buckingham Palace and Holyroodhouse in Scotland, the biannual Investitures, and many other significant events that included the presence of The Queen.

914 Rory, dressed as Page of Honour to the Queen, 1991

Sternfield was sold in 1986. It had been a wonderful home for the family for over forty years, but was no longer a suitable place for us with our family all married with separate lives and children of their own.

In 1991, at the age of 11, our grandson Rory David Arthur Penn became a Page of Honour to The Queen, following his uncle David.

After six years of unproductive house hunting in Scotland we eventually found a delightful early-nineteenth-century former manse in the East Neuk of Fife, sitting high above the fishing village of Pittenweem and overlooking the mouth of the Firth of Forth to the Bass Rock and the Lammermuir hills beyond. We moved in at the end of 1992 and were reunited with all our treasured possessions.

The following spring Eric died very suddenly at the age of seventy-seven after only five months in our new home. The Guards Chapel at Wellington Barracks was full to capacity and more for his funeral, an indication of the affection and respect that so many people had for him.

An extract from an obituary in the *Grenadier Gazette*, the regimental journal of the Grenadier Guards, shows in a gently amusing way the sentiments of his fellow guardsmen.

How one misses Eric, wrote a brother officer. 'As if one heard that Big Ben, with which he had certain affinities, had toppled in to the Thames'. And indeed it is hard to come to terms with the absence of his impeccable erect figure, which for so long graced royal occasions with charm and authority...

His success both as a soldier and courtier, was only partly due to his skills as leader and administrator. His personal qualities counted for even more. His calm imperturbable manner radiated confidence and reassurance. His charm and modesty endeared him to those with whom he worked, and from whom he demanded such high standards. He is very greatly missed...

The Prince of Wales wrote:

...having known Eric all my life, I still cannot believe what has happened. He always seemed utterly indestructible, not to mention indispensable, and the world will be a poorer place without him.

I shall never forget his constant kindness and consideration to me over so many years. Nor will I ever forget his magnificent Grenadier figure, for ever upright and elegant, which dominated so many great events of this country's life. I feel so lucky to have known him and will have such happy and special memories of him...

Charles

Soon after Eric's death The Queen Mother asked me to become one of the extra Ladies in Waiting in her household, an honour and a happiness which only ended with her death in 2002 at the age of one hundred and two. This marked the end of sixty years of royal service by the Penn family.

This book tells the story of the Penn family and the achievements of the marine engineering firm they founded. It shows that we can take pride in their contribution to Victorian Britain, that time when massive advances of technology and industrialisation were visibly reshaping both the landscape and the social structure of a country whose population almost doubled between 1801 and 1851.

I acknowledge the achievement of Richard Hartree's admirable book, and dedicate this Epilogue to my grandson Rory Penn.

Prudence Penn,
Carnbee House, 2008

I am grateful to The Queen and to The Prince of Wales for allowing me to quote from letters of which they hold the copyright.

Appendix 1

List of Penn Patents

Year	Number	Title and details
1845	GB11017	'Steam engines and machinery for propelling vessels applicable to other purposes.' In the names of John Penn, William Hartree, and John Matthew, this is the trunk engine patent.
1848	GB12386	'Marine steam engines.' In the name of John Penn, it relates to improvements in condensers.
1854	GB2114	'Bearings and bushes for the shafts of screw and submerged propellers.' In the name of John Penn, this is the wood (lignum vitae) stern-bearing patent.
1854	GB2258	'Manufacture of the pistons, slide valves and stuffing boxes of marine and other engines.' In the name of John Penn, it relates to the use of wood in these applications.
1857	GB2250	'Apparatus for taking the thrust of screw and submerged propellers.' In the name of John Penn, it relates the use of wood for thrust bearings in this application.
1863	GB572	'Escape or relief valves to the cylinders of marine or other steam engines.' In the name of John Penn, it covers improvements in escape and relief valves.
1870	GB3081	'Improvements in the manufacture of curved metal pipes and in apparatus therein.' In the name of John Penn Junior, it is of doubtful practicality.
1876	GB349	'Steam Engines.' In the name of John Penn, this is the patent covering the three-cylinder compound engine which could work either with one high- and two low-pressure cylinders or with three high-pressure cylinders.
1878	GB222	'Steam Engines.' In the name of John Penn, it makes claims relating to the exhausting of the surface condenser prior to starting the engine.

Appendix 2

Marine Engines made by the Firm

This appendix is based on the information in a database of 775 vessels which had Penn, and TIW/Penn, engines fitted between 1825 and 1911. In 1878 it was claimed that a total of 768 vessels had been fitted with Penn engines. In the database there are 578 to that date. It is assumed that the database includes about 75 per cent of the total and can be used as a representative sample.

Table 1: Totals by Decade

1825-1839	11			
1840-1849	87			
1850-1859	216	(Crimean War)		
1860-1869	170	(Long Slump)		
1870-1879	105	"	(Great Depression)	
1880-1889	44	"	"	
1890-1899	86		"	
1900-1911 (TIW)	56			
Total	775			

1868-1888 was the Long Slump in shipbuilding.
1873-1896 was the Great Depression in the economy.

Table 2: Decade totals by Engine Type

	Drive			Engine					
	Pad	Scr	Oth	Osc	Trnk	Cmp	PtCmp	3x	Other
1825-39	11	-	-	8	-	-	-	-	3
1840-49	81	6	-	82	4	-	-	-	1
1850-59	38	178	-	40	*175	1	-	-	-
1860-69	38	132	-	48	84	-	-	-	38
1870-79	25	80	-	19	29	32	3	2	20
1880-89	14	30	-	16	7	15	2	1	3
1890-99	19	65	-	15	-	11	-	16	**44
1900-11	11	45	2	-	-	21	-	6	***29
Totals	237	536	2	228	299	80	5	25	138

Abbreviations: *Osc* = oscillating; *Cmp* = compound; *PtCmp* = patent compound; *Triple* = triple expansion; *Other* = other and unspecified.

*   Includes 97 RN gunboats and 12 gunboats for foreign navies.
**   Includes 43 RN pinnaces and launches and 2 water-jet Lifeboats.
***   Includes 26 RN pinnaces and 3 turbine-engined ships.

Table 3: Decade totals by end use

	Naval		Merchant	
	British	Foreign	Home*	Foreign
1825-39	1	1	9	-
1840-49	18	11	42	16
1850-59	143	33	19	21
1860-69	68	53	24	25
1870-79	21	26	33	25
1880-89	9	15	14	6
1890-99	**56	-	19	11
1900-11	***35	8	11	2
Totals	351	147	171	106
	498		277	

*   Includes cross-channel and Irish Sea operators, also 18 private yachts.
**   Includes 43 pinnaces and launches.
***   Includes 26 pinnaces and launches.

From Tables 2 and 3, it can be seen that of the total 498 naval vessels only 18 had paddle drive; also that 56 of the 147 foreign naval ships were built in foreign yards, not on Thameside.

Of the 277 Merchant vessels only 47 had screw drive – and of these 17 were yachts. There were only two or three ocean-going merchant vessels. Most were lake, river and coastal steamers, including cross-channel and Irish Sea. Between 1870 and 1900 there were, excluding private yachts, 82 home merchant vessels of which 37 had oscillating engines.

Table 4: Engines by size

	Small	Medium	Large
1825-39	11	-	-
1840-49	70	16	1
1850-59	149	65	2
1860-69	96	60	14
1870-79	62	34	9
1880-89	18	20	6
1890-99	72	6	8
1900-11	47	1	8
Totals	525	202	48

This table is compiled from nhp, ihp, engine size and vessel type information in the database. Broadly, *Small* is up to 100nhp or 1000ihp; *Medium* is from there up to500nhp or 5000ihp; *Large* is above that. These figures show the importance of the smaller engines in the output of the firm.

Table 5: Shipbuilders which used more than 10 Penn engines

Admiralty Dockyards	
Chatham	37
Pembroke	33
Sheerness	15
Devonport	14
Woolwich	11
Total	110
Private Yards	
Thames Ironworks and Shipbuilding	71
Samuda	65
Ditchburn & Mare	56
Pitcher (gunboats)	37
R&H Green	31
Forrestt (pinnaces)	20
C J Mare	18
Crompton (pinnaces)	18
Laird (gunboats)	16
Wigram (4 in Southampton)	15
Rennie	11
Total	358

Laird of Birkenhead is the only yard not on Thameside. This illustrates the closeness of Penn's customer base.

Table 6: End-users which bought 10 or more Penn-engined ships

Navies	
Royal Navy	351
Spain	56
Italy	26
Russia	12
Brazil	11
Germany	10
Total	466
Commercial	
Home	
Waterman Steam Packet Co (Thames)	19
City Boat Co (Thames)	18
P&O	13
LCC (Thames)	11
Overseas	
ROPIT, Russia	12
Russian Steam Navigation and Trading	11
Chirket in Hairie, Turkey	11
Elbe Steamship Co	8 (9 reuses)
Total	103

This provides another picture of the distribution of Penn's business from that in Table 3.

Machinery Costs

In the database machinery costs are given in pounds for many RN ships. The unit £/ihp is a measure of the use of initial capital.

The smallest gunboats, rated at 110ihp, had machinery costs of £1,270 – a £/ihp of 11.5; those rated at 270ihp had a £/ihp of 12.9. Five sailing ships fitted with auxiliary engines in the 1840s give £/ihp values of around 21. For the larger ships of the 1850s the average is 19.2. In the 1860s the average is lower at 11.5 and drops to 8.6 for the trunk engines of the 1770s. The three Penn patent compound/simple engines have an average £/ihp of 16.2 which could have been justified by the lower coal consumption. There are no costs for triple-expansion engine installations.

Crimean War Gunboat engines[1]

During the years 1854–6 there were 156 gunboats built in five classes – 1854 Gleaner 6 and Dapper 20; 1855 Albacore 98 and Cheerful 20; 1856 Clown 12. Penn engines only were used in the Gleaner, Cheerful and Clown classes; a total of 38. Dapper and Albacore classes used Penn and Maudslay engines in equal numbers; that is, 59 each. For Gleaner, Dapper and Albacore Penn supplied twin-cylinder trunk engines of 21in bore x12in stroke, 60nhp and 270ihp operating at 60 psi. Machinery costs were £3,500. This high operating pressure was remarkable for its time and a big step for the Admiralty; at the time large trunk engines were operating at 20 psi. The Maudslay engines also used high pressure. The boilers were cylindrical fire tube locomotive type. For Cheerful and Clown class the engines were not trunk engines but were single-cylinder, single-expansion, single-piston-rod engines, with 15in bore x 12in stroke operating at 60 psi. Cheerful engines are described as 20nhp with a machinery cost of £1,200 and Clown as 40nhp with a machinery cost of £2,400. The difference in power and cost would most readily be explained if Clown class had twin engines.

Information about the Crimean War gunboat engines is confused by the description of the 1867 Beacon Class, the engines of which came from 'rotten-hulled' Crimean War gunboats; twenty-four used Penn engines were installed in twelve of these twin-screw vessels. In the Navy List their cylinder diameter is given as 17.9in which is the diameter of a circle of area equivalent to the annular piston of a trunk engine with a 21in diameter cylinder and an 11in diameter trunk (see Xantho engine, overleaf). It was used in calculations of horsepower and is known as the 'effective diameter'.[2]

Post publication note:-

On 2 July 2008 the American
Society of Mechanical
Engineers designated the
1841 Penn oscillating engine
of the *Diesbar* as a
'Historic Mechanical
Engineering Landmark'.

RH:05/07/08.

Some of the gunboats had fifteen- to twenty-year service lives and some ended up in distant places – Malta, Montevideo, Hong Kong, Shanghai, Japan, and Esquimalt on Vancouver Island.

The *Xantho* Engine

In 1983 the wreck of a small cargo ship, *Xantho,* found at Port Gregory off the west coast of Australia, became the subject of a major marine archaeology project by the Western Australia Maritime Museum. She was discovered to have been powered by a small Crimean War gunboat type of trunk engine. The engine was raised from the seabed, has been recovered, finely restored and reassembled and is on display at the Western Australia Maritime Museum, Shipwreck Galleries, Fremantle. It is the only surviving Penn trunk engine (Plate IVb).

The *Xantho* engine is a 21in diameter x 12in stroke twin-cylinder trunk engine of the type the firm supplied for a large number of Crimean War gunboats. The trunk diameter is 11in. It was fitted in *Xantho* on the Clyde in 1871.

Reviewing the history of the gunboats given in The Navy List it would seem that engines from thirteen vessels could have been available for *Xantho* in 1871; it is not possible to identify which was used.

Penn oscillating engine of PD *Diesbar* at Dresden

This engine was first installed in the paddle steamer *Bohemia* in 1841. Comparison of its design (Plate IVa) with that of a Penn 'Waterman' engine illustrated in *The Engineer* (202, p26) and with the model of an 1842 Penn 'Waterman' engine in the Science Museum shows many common features. It clearly is a Penn design. The illustration (202) shows the valve chests on the cylinder walls at 90° to the line of the crankshaft which is where they are on *Diesbar*; on the model they are offset by 45° towards the pump. The other Penn oscillating engine model in the Science Museum, the model the engine of HMS *Sphinx* (1846) at the Institution of Mechanical Engineers and the *Empress* (1879) engine in the Southampton Maritime Museum all have offset valve chests. It seems that the 90° position was the earliest design.

There have been several recorded changes during the life of the *Diesbar* engine. In 1853 the crankshaft was replaced by Krupp of Essen, with a ten-year guarantee. In 1854 the engine was installed in a new paddle steamer, *Pillnitz*. When installed in *Bohemia* the engine drove the paddles through simple gears so the crankshaft rotated in the opposite direction to the paddles. When installed in *Pillnitz* there was no gearing and the engine was turned through 180° in order to retain the operating layout, with the engineer's controls to the forward and the boilers to the aft. This required the condenser and the controls to be relocated. *Pillnitz* was renamed *Diesbar* in 1924. In 2002 the cylinders and valve chests were replaced.

This note is based on the author's observations during a visit to Dresden, on Sächsishe Dampfschiffahrt publications and on conversations and private communications with Michael Lommatzsch, the 'machine master' on board *Diesbar*.

Huascar and *Esmaralda*

On page 89 of A. Lambert's *Steam, Steel and Shellfire* the vessel *Huascar*, captured by Chile from the Peruvian Navy in the Combat of Iquique in 1879 and now in the Chilean naval museum at Talcahuano, near Concepcion, is described as having 'the only remaining set of Penn trunk engines'. The Chilean report[3] on *Huascar* states that she was built by Laird of Birkenhead and that 'La maquina principal era una Maudslay de biela de connexion indirecta . . . con el cual se obtiene el mismo objetivo de la Maquina de tronco de Penn'; that is, it is a 'Maudslay indirect engine . . . which meets the same design objectives as the Penn trunk engine'. (Reading this dashed my hope of ever seeing a real Penn trunk engine, until I learnt of *Xantho*. RH.)

A smaller Chilean Navy vessel, *Esmaralda*, was sunk in this engagement and has been found on the seabed some 40m deep. She was built by Pitcher. A Penn engine nameplate has been recovered from the wreck. Conditions have so far prevented the engine from being further identified. It is probably a 2x21x12in trunk engine, like *Xantho*. This information is from private communications from Pedro Campos.

The Penn engine database

Most of the data for these tables was provided by Brian Hillsdon from his own researches and those of Paul Blackburn; some came from the author's researches. Mr Hillsdon had the opportunity to proofread *The Sail and Steam Navy List* by D. Lyon and R. Winfield, which led to some extra information. Both he and Mr Blackburn proofread the database table. The information on the Elbe steamers came from Johannes Hirsch[4] and that about several Spanish naval ships from Edward Sargent.[5]

The Access database which holds this information has Fields for: Year; Vessel name; Drive; End Use; Engine type; Owner/ Operator; Vessel type; Shipbuilder; nhp; ihp; Cylinder diameter and stroke (to nearest inch); Boiler psi and type; Machinery price. All fields are not complete for every entry. The tabulation can be provided on disc for those with Microsoft Access or as a printout in Year or Vessel name order. Price £7.00. All proceeds to the Penn Almshouse Trust. Anyone interested please contact the author on richard@hartree.org.uk.

Appendix 3

Marine Engine Builders of the 1800s

The following tables give a picture of the industrial context within which John Penn and Sons carried on its business.

Table 1: Lifespans of 16 major Thameside Shipbuilding and Marine Engineering Firms

1.	Millwall Ironworks	1861-1866	5 years
2.	William Fairbairn	1835-1849	14
3.	Dudgeon	1859-1875	16
4.	John Scott Russell	1844-1861	17
5.	Ditchburn & Mare	1837-1856	19
6.	Seaward & Capel	1824-1858	34
7.	Thorneycroft	1864-1907	43
8.	Yarrow	1860-1907	47
9.	Samuda	1843-1893	50
10.	Miller & Barnes	1822-1872	50
11.	C. J. Mare/ Thames Iron Works	1856-1912	56
12.	Humphrys, Tennant & Dykes	1852-1908	56
13.	R.& H. Green	1843-1901	58
14.	Rennie	1821-1915	94
15.	Maudslay Son & Field	1797-1904	107
16.	John Penn & Son/ TIW	1799-1899/1911	100/110

This data was taken from Banbury P, Shipbuilding on the Thames and Medway with alterations from the writer's research for Maudslay and Penn data.

Table 2: Engine Builders to the Royal Navy, 1825 -89.

Engine Builder	1825-1839	1840-1849	1850-1859	1860-1869	1870-1879	1880-1889	Total
Boulton & Watt	9	6	2				17
Humphrys Tennant			7	17	20	16	20
Maudsley	8	12	110	31	8	16	185
R Napier	2	4	5	25	9	5	50
Penn	1	19	142	38	21	8	229
Ravenhill*		12	35	19	21		87
Rennie*		7	5	9	11	13	45
Seaward Capel	9	19	2				30
Others	7	20	26	23	51	68	195
Total	36	99	334	162	141	126	898

*Family name used by three firms.

This data, for fighting ships excluding Torpedo boats, was taken from The Navy List. From 1825 -89 thirty-eight firms, using thirty two family names, supplied engines to the Royal Navy. Twenty-four each supplied less than twenty-four engines and twelve supplied between ten and forty-nine. The dominance of Penn and Maudslay up to the 1870s is clear. The increase in Others in the 1870s and 80s is largely from the 'northern', and other, yards away from London.

Appendix 4

Penn Almshouses

These are described in Chapter 6, p86; see also plates Ib and the back cover illustration.

They are now known as the Penn and Widow Smith Almshouses. The Penn and Fairbanks-Smith families are still active in the running of the trust which owns the Almshouses and has the responsibility for their maintenance and modernisation. The original endowments have been exhausted and funds are required for the upgrading of the buildings.

The Almshouses are the only living memorial to the achievements of John Penn and Sons and the contributions the firm made to the development of marine engineering and to the development of the community of Greenwich. The authors have decided that any royalties they may receive from the publication of this book will go to the Penn and Widow Smith Almshouses Trust. If any reader wishes to make a donation it should be sent to:

Mark Fairbanks-Smith
Trustee Penn and Widow Smith Almshouses Trust
Baring Asset Management Limited
155 Bishopsgate
London
EC2M 3XY

Appendix 5

Places to visit and things to see

Deptford

Deptford Works site (grid reference TQ372781)

This can be reached from the A200. Take the turn to the north (towards the river) opposite Deptford High Street. It is called Watergate Street. Follow it to the right turn onto Borthwick Street. Park near there. The site was on the downstream side of Watergate Street as it continues as a footpath with stairs to the riverside. The arched riverfront of the Works building can be seen from the mudflats. If you go down watch out for a rising tide. At the corner of Watergate and Borthwick Streets there is a simple cast-iron bollard which bears the name of John Penn, not easy to read [301, p34]. Both the arched riverfront and the bollard are scheduled. The whole area is subject to a planning application for development. Nearby St Nicholas Church is worth a visit.

Deptford works, waterfront

Greenwich

Greenwich Works site
(grid reference TQ 377767)

This can be reached from the A2. It is on the south side of Blackheath Road, just before the name changes to Blackheath Hill, and the crossroads with Greenwich South Street and Lewisham Road, A2211. Up the Lewisham Road the first turning on the right is John Penn Street [101, p12]. The site was between Blackheath Road and John Penn and Franklin Streets. The upper part is now occupied by a DIY store and a pet food outlet. The goods entrance for the DIY store is approximately where Penn's works entrance was. It is possible to walk right around the upper part of the site and to appreciate that it was far from level. The lower part is now a housing development.

Coldbath Row, where John Penn II, William Penn and William and Charlotte Hartree lived in 1841 was the name given to the row of houses on the south side of Blackheath Road above the footpath through to John Penn Street and backing onto the Works site; it is shown on Morris's 1832 map of Greenwich.

Penn Almshouses (grid reference TQ 381769)

These are in Greenwich South Street, a short walk from the A2/A2211 crossroads by the Works site, on the right-hand side. It is a quality building and well worth a look [Plate Ib and 601, p85]. The residents are friendly towards interested visitors.

Lee

The Cedars (grid reference TQ 387762)

This is the Italianate mansion created by John Penn II and where his family grew up. His widow Ellen lived there until 1911. From the A20 at Lee Bridge turn left on the B220, Belmont Hill. After passing Belmont Grove on the left, north, side the gate lodge built by John Penn II can be seen. It is now the entrance to a residential development which includes The Cedars, divided into flats, and several modern apartment buildings. It is possible to park and walk about. The Cedars is best seen from the north rather than the side facing Belmont Hill. It is hard to gain a good impression of the place as in the Penns' day.

St Margaret's Church

(grid reference TQ 387757)

The church is on the right-hand, south, side when coming up Belmont Hill beyond The Cedars between Brandram Road and Church

The Cedars front, 2002

Terrace. It is the church where the Penn family regularly worshiped and for which John Penn II bought the pews. Inside is a memorial plaque to Ellen. In the graveyard, just to the north of the west end of the church is the Penn family vault. The inscriptions are very hard to read.

Lewisham

Riverdale House and Mill

The mill in Molesworth Street, opposite the Lewisham Centre with a CitiBank sign on it, was part of the property of John Penn I which was associated with Riverdale House. All the other buildings associated with the Penns in Lewisham have gone.

Museums and Ships

National Science Museum, Kensington

In the Marine Engineering gallery models of several Penn engines are displayed. There are moving models of oscillating and trunk engines which are helpful to an understanding of the development described in the text. There are models of many others made by competing firms. There is also the Symington engine of 1788 which was rebuilt by Penn.

Also at the Science Museum Blythe Street store (view by appointment only) is the stern bearing bush from SS Royal Charter, a Gibbs, Bright & Co vessel which served on the Australia route. She was wrecked off Anglesey in 1859. The stern bush recovered from the wreck had served for 200,000 miles [305, p41].

There are also models of an oscillating engine and a trunk engine at the Institution of Mechanical Engineers in Birdcage Walk.

HMS Warrior

This splendid ship lies within the Portsmouth Historic Dockyard complex and is one of the major attractions. She has been restored to her original appearance and replica engines have been installed [Plate IIIb]. She makes a fine place to learn about the mid-Victorian Navy and to see a trunk engine turning.

Maritime Museum, Southampton

The oscillating engine from the 1879 paddle steamer Empress is on display [601, p85]

Western Australia Maritime Museum, Shipwreck Galleries, Fremantle

The engine of the Xantho and other items which have been recovered from the wreck are displayed. The engine is a Penn gunboat engine like those built for the Crimean War [307, p46, Plate IVb and Appendix 2, p118].

Dresden, Diesbar

This paddle steamer is operated by the Sächsische Dampfschiffahrtsgesellschaft GmbH & Co. Conti Elbschiffahrts KG (The Saxony Steamship Company). This company, with various name changes, has operated steamships on the Elbe since 1836. Its nine steam paddle steamers constitute the oldest and largest fleet of paddle steamers in the world. They operate cruises and charters. Enquiries can be made through the website www.saechsische-dampfschiffahrt.de.

Diesbar [204, p28], originally named Pillnitz, was built in 1884 at Dresden and fitted with a Penn oscillating engine of 1841 [Plate IVa and 208, p32] which had previously been in Bohemia [203, p28 and Appendix 2, p118].

Referenced Sources

1. Books

Arnold, A. J., *Iron Shipbuilding on the Thames, 1832–1915,* Ashgate, 2000.

Atkinson, Norman, *Sir Joseph Whitworth,* Sutton, 1996.

Banbury, P., Shipbuilders of the Thames and Medway, David and Charles, 1971.

Barry, P, *Dockyard Economy and Naval Power*, T. Danks, 1863.

Bathe, Greville and Dorothy, *Jacob Perkins*, Historical Society of Pennsylvania, 1943.

Briggs, Sir J. H., *Naval Administrations, 1827-1892.* ed. Lady Briggs. Sampson Low, 1897.

Bourne, John, *Treatise on Steam*, Longmans Green, 3rd edition, 1853 and 5th edition, 1861.

Budrith, J., *Never Forget,* private publication.

Cantrell, John and Cookson, Gillian, *Henry Maudslay and the Pioneers of the Machine Age*, Tempus, 2002.

Coad, Jonathan, *The Royal Dockyards 1690–1850*, Scolar, c.1989.

Dews, Nathaniel, *History of Deptford*, Simpkin, Marshall, 1884.

Emmerson, George S., *The Greatest Iron Ship: SS Great Eastern*, David and Charles, 1991.

Fairbairn, Sir William, *Autobiography*, Longmans Green, 1877.

Gardiner, R. and Greenhill, B. *The Advent of Steam*, Conway, 1993.

Gavin, C. M., *Royal Yachts,* Rich and Cowan, 1932.

Greenhill, Basil and Giffard, Ann, *The British Assault on Finland 1854–5: A Forgotten Naval War*, Conway Maritime Press, 1988.

Griffiths, Denis, *Steam at Sea*, Conway Maritime Press, 1997.

Hart, F. H., *History of Lee and its Neighbourhood*, Conway Maritime Press, 1971.

Hobsbawm, E. J., *Industry and Empire*, Pelican Books, 1969.

Lambert, A, *Steam, Steel and Shellfire*, Conway Maritime Press, 1992.

Lambert, A. D., *Battleships in Transition: The Creation of the Steam Battlefleet 1815–1860*, Conway Maritime Press, 1984.

Lambert, Andrew D, *The Crimean War. British Grand Strategy Against Russia 1853–56*, Manchester University Press, 1990.

Lloyds Register of Yachts, 1879.

Lyon, D. and Winfield, R., *The Sail and Steam Navy List. All the ships of the Royal Navy 1815–1889*, Chatham, 2004.

Moffat, Hugh, *Ipswich Ships and Shipyards 1700–1970*, Malthouse Press, 2002.

Newman, Peter C., *Caesars of the Wilderness*, Penguin Books, 1988.

Otway, Robert, *Elementary Treatise on Steam*, London, 1834.

Penn, G., *Up Funnel, Down Screw*, Hollis and Carter, 1955.

Rennie, Sir John, *Autobiography*, E&FN Spon, 1875.

Rolt, L. T. C., *Isambard Kingdom Brunel*, Penguin Books, 1989.

Ross, Capt. John, *Treatise on Navigation by Steam, and an Essay towards a System of Naval Tactics peculiar to Steam Navigation*, London, 1828.

Smiles, Aileen, *Samuel Smiles and his Surroundings*, Robert Hale, 1956.

Smiles, Robert, *Great Industries of Great Britain, Vol 1*, Cassell, Petter and Galpin, 1880/4.

Smiles, Samuel, *Industrial Biography*, John Murray, 1863.

Smith, E. C., *A Short History of Naval and Marine Engineering*, Cambridge University Press, 1937.

Spater, George, *William Cobbett: the poor man's friend*, Cambridge University Press, 1982.

Spratt, H. P, *Handbook of Collections Illustrating Marine Engineering*, Science Museum, HMSO, 1953.

Uglow, Jenny, *The Lunar Men*, Faber and Faber, 2002.

Watson, Julian, *Some Greenwich Charities*.

Wells, Capt. John, *The Immortal Warrior*, Kenneth Mason, 1997.

Who was Who.

Wisden and *Wisden County Cricket Book.*

2. Journals and Newspapers

The Blackheath Local Guide and Advertiser (Blackheath)

Country Life

Eberbacher Gesschitsblat [in German]

The Engineer

Engineering

Engineering in Miniature

Greenwich Industrial History Society (GIHS)

The Illustrated London News

Journal of the Dorking Local History Group (JDLHG)

Journal of the Ordnance Society (JOS)

Journal of the Royal Aeronautical Society (JRAeS)

The Kentish Mercury and Greenwich Gazette (The Kentish Mercury)

The Lewisham Gazette

Mariner's Mirror (MM)

Proceedings of the Institution of Civil Engineers (ProcICE)

Proceedings of the Institute of Marine Engineers (ProcIMarE)

Proceedings of the Institution of Mechanical Engineers (ProcIMechE).

Proceedings of the Institution of Naval Architect (ProcINA)

Shipbuilding on the Thames and Thames-Built Ships, Proceedings of a Second Symposium, held 15 Feb 2003. Ed.& Publ. Dr Roger Owen (*Shipbuilding on the Thames*)

Thames Ironworks Gazette (TIW Gazette)

The Times

Transactions of the Newcomen Society (TransNSoc)

3. Others

Alumni Cantabrigiensis, Venn

Captain's Letter Book, HMS *Warrior*, 1861 to 1864 (*Captain's Letters*)

Garcia, R., 'Restoring the Xantho Engine', Western Australian Maritime Museum, 2004: www.museum.wa.gov.au/collections/maritime/march/shipwrecks/Xantho/Xantho.html

Hansard

Hayward's Patent Cases

HMS *Warrior*, Guide

Historikkreis-Elbe-Schiffarht, Dresden, (*HES*) [in German]

McCarthy, M., 'The Xantho Excavation 1983–95', Western Australian Maritime Museum, 2003: www.museum.wa.gov.au/collections/maritime/march/shipwrecks/Xantho/Xantho.html

Monitor Huscar, a Chilean Navy report, Editorial Lamas y Cia. [in Spanish]

Official Catalogue of the Great Exhibition of the Works of All Nations, 1851

Programme for a concert at the Barbican Hall, 1998

Programme for the Opening of the Royal Albert Hall, 1871

The Royal Naval College, Guide

Thames Ironworks, Shipbuilding and Engineering Ltd, Historical Catalogue for the 1911 Empire Exhibition at the Crystal Palace (*TIW Historical Catalogue*)

Timbs, John, *The Industry, Science and Art of the Age*. International Exhibition of 1862

Notes and References

None of the firm's records still exist. There is little unpublished material about the Penn family and firm. Some was found in the archives at the IMechE, the Science Museum library and in Hartree and Penn family records – notably J. Coomber's letter to John Penn II of 7 December 1877. The published material is very scattered. References have been restricted to matters directly related to the history of the firm and family.

Chapter 1, Background and Early Years

1 Private communication, Pieter Van der Merwe.
2 ICE Annual Report for 1843, pp13–14; ProcICE Vol 59, p298; The Kentish Mercury 28/09/1878.
3 Smiles, Samuel, p116.
4 Cantrell and Cookson, Chapter 3.
5 Atkinson, p19.
6 Smiles, Samuel, pp236–57 and Cantrell and Cookson, Chapters 3 and 6.
7 ICE references in note 2 above.
8 Cantrell and Cookson, p46
9 Will of John Penn I.
10 ICE membership records, Hartree family records.
11 Proc ICE Vol 59, p299 and The Kentish Mercury 28/09/1878.
12 Uglow, p vi.
13 Cantrell and Cookson, p47.
14 Cantrell and Cookson, p51.

Chapter 2, Into Steam

1 Re Ipswich and Suffolk, Moffat, pp39–45 and Sci Mus Lib ARCH FIELD 1/2,1/37–9.
2 Re Perkins, ProcICE Vol 59, pp300–1; JOS Vol 11, pp67–75; Bathe, pp128–13.
3 The Engineer, 4 Oct 1878.
4 Penn family records – J. Coomber letter.
5 ProcICE Vol 59, p300.
6 Penn, G., p31.
7 As best as could be ascertained. PRO ADM 181/42, Navy Estimates, show a big increase in Bakery staffing for 1833.
8 Smiles, R., p59, also Hobsbawm, p76 note, Rennie p412 and Coad on Plymouth and Portsmouth VictuallingYards.
9 Smiles, R, p59.
10 The Times, 11 Dec 1832.
11 Spater, p172, p278 note 63 and p283 note 86.
12 TransNSoc Vol 57, p126, and Banbury, p139.
13 Newman, pp288–90.
14 Otway and Ross.
15 As Appendix 2.
16 Arnold, p27.
17 www.saechsische-dampfschiffahrt.de and HES No86 (2004) pp3, 5, 6 and 10; also No 35 (1997) pp2–5.
18 Eberbacher Geschsblatt, Mai 1993 p116 and pp144–9.
19 The Engineer, 10 Dec 1897 and Sci Mus Lib ARCH GOOD 1760.
20 E. C. Smith in TransNSoc, Vol 2, p88.
21 Ibid.
22 Sci Mus Lib Archive, MS 1461.
23 The Kentish Mercury, 10 Jun 1843.

Chapter 3, Success with Steam

1 Rennie, pp414–5.
2 TransNSoc, Vol 2, p 92.
3 ICE membership records and 1851 Census.
4 1845 patent GB 11017.
5 Bourne, 5th ed, p313–4 and p404.
6 IMechE archive, GB 381, IMS 170.
7 TransNSoc, Vol 19, p160.
8 The Navy List, p211.
9 Arnold, p29.
10 Royal Archives, RA PP/YACHTS/14.

11 As Appendix 2.
12 As Chapter 2, note 18.
13 ProcICE, Vol59, p300.
14 Banbury, p226, and ICE Membership records.
15 Gardiner, Robert, ed., p31–2.
16 Lambert, Andrew, p40.
17 The Times, 14 Jul 1851.
18 The Times, 31 Jan 1852.
19 Royal Archive, RA PP/YACHTS/38.
20 1854 patent GB 2114 and Haywood's Patent Cases 1600–1883 Vol 8, pp933–74.
21 Penn, G., p79.
22 Briggs, p109.
23 Greenhill and Giffard, p337.
24 MM, Vol 51 (May 1966) and ProcICE Vol 59, p304.
25 Atkinson, p109.
26 Author's observation – during concert at the Newbury Festival.
27 McCarthy; also Garcia.
28 Hart, p23, Kentish Mercury 28 Sep 1878 and private communication – Neil Burton, a report for English Heritage.
29 Hartree family records.
30 ProcICE, 1869, Memoir for John Matthew and JDLHG, 1998, pp1–7.
31 Rolt, p320.
32 Bourne, 3rd ed, p243.
33 Spratt, also Marine Engineering display at Science Museum.

Chapter 4, A Very Reputable Firm

1 Briggs, p137.
2 ProcINA, 5 Jul 1911, 'Fifty Years Changes in British Warship Machinery', p111.
3 TrnsNSoc, Vol 58, p95.
4 As Appendix 2.
5 Royal Society, ref A05545.
6 ProcICE, Vol 59, p307.
7 Sci Mus Lib, MS 1447.
8 The Kentish Mercury, 12 Feb 1859.
9 The Kentish Mercury, 19 Feb 1859.
10 Hartree family records.
11 ProcIMechE, 1859, pp195–202.
12 The Times, 2 Feb, 25 Jun and 28 Dec 1860.
13 Rolt, pp375–6, and Emmerson, p68 and p98.
14 HMS Warrior Guide, and Wells.
15 The Engineer, 1 Jan 1861.
16 Bourne, 5th ed, p404.
17 Bourne, 5th ed, p314.
18 ProcIMarE, 23 Oct 1990 reprint.
19 Captain's Letters, Capt. Cochrane letter of 11 Dec 1861.
20 Wells, p221.
21 Smiles, Samuel, p182.
22 Engineering in Miniature, January 2004, p216.
23 The Times, 26 July 1861.
24 Penn family records.
25 Private communication from the Victoria and Albert Museum.
26 Sci Mus Lib, ARCH MAUD 17/24.
27 GIHS, September 2007, Vol 9 no 5, p6.
28 Smiles, Aileen, pp93, 96 and 106.
29 The Engineer, Vol 81, 14 Jun 1861.
30 The Times, 14 May 1862.

31 As Chapter 2, note 18.
32 Gavin, App 1 pp278/9.
33 Royal Archive, RA VIC9ADD A15 /255.
34 See Appendix 2.
35 Blackheath, 10 Nov 1934, p24
36 Private communication, Johannes Hirsch.
37 The Times, 19 July 1863.
38 Cantrell and Cookson, p175.
39 Hartree family records.
40 Smiles, Aileen, p106.
41 Barry, p267.
42 The Engineer, Sep 1938.

Chapter 5, The Coming of the Compound

1 Haywood's Patent Cases, Vol 8, pp933–74.
2 IMechE Council minute, 11 Nov 1866.
3 The Engineer, Vol 31 (1871), p34.
4 IMechE Council minute, 28 Oct 1869.
5 Emmerson, pp120–135.
6 ProcIMechE, Vol 18 (1867), pp44–5.
7 Emmerson, p97 and pp162–4.
8 Fairbairn, p277.
9 ProcICE, 1869 pp446–8, memoir for John Matthew.
10 Venn, Alumni Cantabrigiensis, p84 and Harrow School.
11 1870 patent GB 3081.
12 Arnold, p102.
13 See Appendix 2.
14 NSW Heritage Office. John Penn Report, Underwater Archaeological Research Group. 1984.
15 Lambert, Andrew, p83.
16 Smith, p162.
17 Blackheath, 17 November 1934, p24.
18 Illustrated London News, 1 and 8 Apr 1871, p311, p326 and p342 and The Engineer, May 1871, p39.
19 Barbican concert programme, 21 Nov 1998.
20 JRAeS, Vol 61 (Mar 1957), pp160–1.
21 Undated from Nature, Penn family records.
22 TransNSoc, Vol 76, 1, p141.
23 Grand Fancy Bazaar programme, Greenwich Local History Library, Penn file.
24 Hart, p24.
25 ICE and IMechE membership records.
26 Hobsbawm, p127.
27 Lloyds register of Yachts, 1879.
28 Deduced from the will of John Penn II.
29 1876 patent GB349.
30 Engineering, 9 April 1880, p271.
31 Engineering, 17 February 1888, p158.
32 IMechE minute books, 1877–82.
33 Penn family records, J Coomber letter.
34 The Kentish Mercury, 5 Oct 1878.
35 The Kentish Mercury, 28 Sep 1978.
36 The Engineer, 4 Oct 1878.
37 The Kentish Mercury, 5 Oct 1878.
38 Penn family records; Epilogue p[PAGE REF].
39 The Kentish Mercury, 5 Oct 1878.
40 Proc ICE, Vol 59, p307.
41 The Kentish Mercury, 5 Oct 1878.
42 NMSI collection at National Railway Museum, York, ref 1998-8350.

Chapter 6, The Next Generation

1 Penn, G., p110, E. J. Reed letter to The Times, 1877.
2 Penn, G., p124.
3 Smiles, R., pp59–64.
4 From Wisden publications.
5 Private communication, Neil Rhind.
6 Daws, p304.
7 Watson, pp100–1. Also Kentish Mercury, November 1884 and February 1885.
8 PRO BT31/4514/29492.

9 See Appendix 2.
10 Engineering, Vol.LIX (Jan–Jun 1895), pp485–6.
11 Who was Who, 1897–1911.
12 The Times, 27 Aug 1891.
13 Hansard, 1891–1903.
14 ProcICE, Vol 119, p75, contribution of Prof. J. H. Biles.
15 Hansard, 1891–1903.
16 The Times, 23 Nov 1903.
17 The Kentish Mercury, 4 Dec 1903 and Blackheath, 5 Dec 1903.
18 Ibid.
19 Ibid.
20 TransNSoc, 1922 (Vol 2), p114.
21 The Times, 20 Jul 1897.
22 The Times, 1 Aug 1897.
23 The Kentish Mercury, 9, 16 and 22 Jul 1897.
24 Guildhall Library MS 19096 and PRO Company reports.
25 Penn, G., p140.
26 The Kentish Mercury, 4 Dec 1903 and Blackheath, 5 Dec 1903.
27 Ibid.
28 Ibid.
29 Ibid.
30 Budrith, pp 177–8.
31 The Kentish Mercury, 1 Dec 1911 and Blackheath, 9 Dec 1911.

Chapter 7, Under New Management

1 Arnold, pp134–40.
2 The Times, 4 Apr 1901.
3 Guildhall Library MS 19096.
4 Metropolitan Archives 0/45/1 and PRO BT 31/1722/6293 and 31/16240/62972; TIW Gazettes, Jul 1899–Oct 1906.
5 Metropolitan Archives 0/45/1 and PRO BT 31/1722/6293 and 31/16240/62972.
6 Metropolitan Archives 0/45/1 and PRO BT 31/1722/6293 and 31/16240/62972; TIW Gazettes, Jul 1899–Oct 1906.
7 Ibid.
8 Ibid.
9 Ibid.
10 TIW Historical Catalogue.
11 Arnold, pp147–9.
12 The Times, 15 Nov 1911.
13 Ibid.
14 Private communication, Michael Wright – Fuller, Horsey, Sons & Cassell catalogue for sale, 27 May 1913.

Appendix 2

1 Navy List, pp224–30 and 294.
2 The 'effective' diameter of a trunk engine is the diameter of the circle with the same area as the annular piston. It is the value used to calculate horsepower. In The Navy List it is not made clear whether the cylinder diameters given for trunk engines are 'effective' or 'actual'. The labels on trunk engine models in the Science Museum collection show 'effective' diameters which agree with the diameters given for those ships in The Navy List. The Gleaner, Dapper and Albacore gunboat data gives the actual diameters.
3 Chilean Navy report, Monitor Huascar.
4 HES No86 (2004) pp3–6 and 10, also No35 (1997) pp2–5.
5 Sargent, E., 'Some Steam Warships supplied to the Spanish Navy in the 19th Century', in Owen, R. (ed.), Shipbuilding on the Thames, 2004, p104.

Index

(entries in *italics* are ships' names)

Admiralty
Aeronautical Society
HMS *Agamemnon*
Albert Victor
RY *Alberta*
HMS *Alecto*
Archimedes
HMS *Arethusa*
HMS *Arrogant*

Baltic Sea
Banshee
Barry, P.
Beaver
Black Eagle
Blackheath
    Horticultural Society
    Road
    Royal Golf Club
HMS *Black Prince*
Black Sea
Bohemia
Boulton, Matthew
Brazil
Briggs, Sir J.H.
Brunel, I.K.
Brunel, Marc
Boulton & Watt
Bourne, John
Burford Lodge

Carlton House Terrace
Carnatic
The Cedars
City of Glasgow
Clement, Joseph
Cherbourg Strategy
Chile
China
Churchill, Winston
Clermont
Clyde
Cobbett, William
Comet
HMS *Constance*
Coomber, John
HMS *Cornwallis*
Country Life
Crimea
Cristoforo Columbo
Cubitt, William/Sir

Dartmouth, Earl of
Deptford
Deutschland
HMS *Devastation*
Diesbar
Ditchburn, Thomas
Donkin, Bryan
Driver
Dundas, Capt./Admiral
Dwarf

Election (Parliamentary) 1832
    1891
    1892
Elfin
HMS *Encounter*
Engineers in the Navy

Fairbairn, William/Sir
Fairy
Field, Joshua
HMS *Firebrand*
France

Germany
La Gloire
HMS *Goliath*
Great Britain
Great Eastern
Great Exhibition, 1851
Greenwich
Gunboats
    Engines

Hartree,
    Charlotte, nee Penn
    John Penn
    Maria
    William I
    William II
Hedges, John
HMS *Hercules*
Hills, Arnold T.
House of Commons
Howard, Thomas
Humphreys, Edward
Humphreys, Tennant & Dykes

Independecia
HMS *Inflexible*
Institution of Civil Engineers
Institution of Mechanical Engineers
Institution of Naval Architects
Inkerman
Ipswich
Italy

Japan
John Penn, cross-channel packet
John Penn, Elbe steamer
John Penn 2
John Penn Street
John Penn's Band

Kaiser
Kronstadt

Lara
Lee
Lewisham
Lewisham Road
Lignum vitae
London
Louise Dagmar

HMS *Magnificent*
Malacca
Margery
Mary Beatrice
Maritime Greenwich
Matthew, John
Maudslay, Henry
Maudslay, Sons & Field
Monarch
Morden Hill

Napier, David
Napoleon III
HMS *Neptune*

HMS *Northampton*
HMS *Northumberland*
Nunhead Cemetery

Octavia
Oscillating Engine

Pandora
Pandora
Patent
Penn Almshouses
Penn
    Amy (nee Lucas)
    Arthur
    Constance, Connie (nee Lucas)
    Ellen, nee English
    Eric
    Eric Frank
    Frank
    Frankie
    John I
    John II
    John III
    Thomas
    William
Perkins, Jacob
Peru
HMS *Phoenix*
Portugal

HMS *Rattler*
Rennie, John/Sir
HMS *Retribution*
Rotherhithe
Royal Albert Hall
Royal Yachts
Royal Society
Russia

HMS *Sappho*
HMS *Sappho* (2)
St. Margaret's Church, Lee
Sevastopol
Smiles, R.
Smiles, Samuel
Smith, Francis Petit
Spain
Starley, James
Stephenson, Robert/Sir
Suffolk
Symington, William

Taverham Hall
Thames
Thames
Thames Ironworks
HMS *Thunderer*
Trunk Engine

Victoria and Albert 1 & 2

HMS *Warrior*
Watt, James
Westminster
Whitworth, Joseph/Sir
Wilton Crescent
Woolwich

Xantho

Index

(entries in *italics* are ships' names)

Admiralty
25, 33, 37, 38, 40, 43, 49, 52, 58, 61
Albert, Prince, Duke of York,
later King George VI 112
Aeronautical Society 73
HMS *Agamemnon* 39
RY *Alberta* 58
HMS *Alecto* 34
Archimedes 27
HMS *Arethusa* 69
HMS *Arrogant* 39

Baltic 42, 43
Banshee 33
Barry, P. 61
Beaver 25
Beaufort Gardens 111
Birkhall 113
Black Eagle 33
Blackheath
Horticultural Society 57, 74
Royal Golf Club 85
HMS *Black Prince* 97
Black Sea 42, 44
Bohemia 72, 59
Boulton, Matthew 15
Brazil 50, 59
Briggs, Sir J.H. 42, 45, 49
Brunel, I.K. 27
Boulton & Watt 23, 33
Bourne, John 21, 31, 35, 47, 78
Burford Lodge 47

Carnatic 69
Carnbee House 117
The Cedars
47, 50, 56, 57, 80, 104, 124
Charles, Prince of Wales 117
Chelsea Square 114
Cherbourg Strategy 39, 42
Chile 121
Churchill, Winston 99
City of Glasgow 92
Clarence House 114
Clement, Joseph 11, 14, 60
Clermont 13
Clyde 15
Cobbett, William 24
Comet 22
HMS *Constance* 69
HMS *Cornwallis* 42
Crimea 44
Cristoforo Columbo 75
Cubitt, William/Sir 14, 19

Dartmouth, Earl of 12, 90
Deptford 12, 23, 33
Deutschland 74
HMS *Devastation* 72, 82
Diesbar 27, 59, 121, 124
Ditchburn, Thomas 21, 27, 29, 37
Donkin, Bryan 12
Dundas, Capt./Admiral 24, 44
Dwarf 29

Election (Parliamentary) 1832 24
1891 90
1892 91
Elbe 59, 124
Elizabeth, Queen, formerly Lady
Elizabeth Bowes-Lyon and
Duchess of York 112

Elizabeth II, Queen 114
Empress 85
HMS *Encounter* 36
Engineers in the Navy
23, 37, 45, 72, 83, 91, 94
Eugenie, Empress 106

Fairbairn, William/Sir 12, 13, 40, 80
Fairy 37
Field, Joshua 40, 50, 51, 52
France 41

Germany 50, 59
La Gloire 52
Gloucester Square 108
Great Britain 27, 40
Great Eastern 52, 71, 82
Great Exhibition, 1851 39
Gunboats 42
Engines 43, 120

Hartree, Charlotte (nee Penn),
13, 14, 28, 61
John Penn (Jack) 61
Maria 34
William 14, 22, 25, 28, 51
William II 93
Hedges, John 28, 37, 58
HMS *Hercules* 67
Hills, Arnold F 98
Himalaya 35
House of Commons 91, 93
Howard, Thomas 14, 28, 31, 51
Humphrys, Edward 38
Humphrys, Tennant & Dykes
49, 93, 99

Independecia 74
Institution of Civil Engineers
15, 21, 36, 82
Institution of Mechanical Engineers
38, 50, 41, 70, 74, 75, 80
Institution of Naval Architects 52
Inkerman 27
Ipswich 19
Italia 75
Italy 59

Japan 50, 59
John Penn, cross-channel packet, 51
John Penn, Elbe steamer 59
John Penn, Aust 72
John Penn's Band 73

Kaiser 74
Kronstadt 42

Lara 75
Lee 46
Lewisham 29, 37, 124
Lignum vitae 40, 48, 69, 71, 93
Lisbon Trials 38

HMS *Magnificent* 89
Malacca 53
St. Margaret's Church, Lee 106
Margery 14
Matthew, John 14, 28, 34, 71
Maudslay, Henry 11, 12, 80
Maudslay, Sons & Field
23. 33, 43, 60, 99
The Castle of Mey 113
Morden Hill 47, 57
Napier, David 47

Napoleon III, Emperor of the French
38, 41, 73, 106
HMS *Neptune* 74
Newton House 108
HMS *Northampton* 75, 82

Octavia 69
Oscillating Engine 26, 92

Pandora 57
Pandora 75, 77
Patent engine (1876) 75
Penn Almshouses 86, 123
Penn, Arthur 109, 110, 112, 113
Constance, Connie (nee Lucas)
106
Ellen (nee English)
37, 80, 84, 95, 109
Eric 111, 114
Eric Frank 108
Frank 95
John I 9, 14, 19
John II 11, 13, 21, 22,
27, 29, 40, 41, 42, 52, 60, 77, 80
John II
71, 74, 75, 88, 90. 93, 94, 106
Thomas 14, 33, 75, 87
William 14, 29, 56
William, son of John II
71, 74, 88, 84, 93, 97, 106, 111
Perkins, Jacob 21, 22, 31
Peru 50, 59
HMS *Phoenix* 36

HMS *Rattler* 34
Rennie, John/Sir 12, 23
HMS *Retribution* 33
Royal Albert Hall 72
Royal Yachts 37, 40
Royal Society 50
Russia 27, 41, 59

HMS *Sappho* 68
HMS *Sappho (2)* 89
St. Margaret's Church, Lee 77, 124
Sevastopol 42
Smiles, Robert 83
Smiles, Samuel 53, 60
Smith, Francis Petit 27, 40
Spain 59
Starley, James 73
Sternfield House 113
Stephenson, Robert/Sir 35, 50
Suffolk 19
Symington, William 10, 48

Taverham Hall 107
Thames 14
Thames Ironworks 53, 93
HMS *Thunderer* 98
Trunk Engine 35, 39, 49, 53, 72

RY *Victoria and Albert 1 & 2* 58, 59

Watt, James 16, 80
HMS *Warrior* 52, 53, 82, 83, 124
Whitworth, Joseph/Sir 11, 41, 74, 80
Wilton Crescent 112
HMS *Windsor Castle* 51

Xantho 45, 121